BROKEN STICK

BROKEN STICK

MISSION TO THE FORBIDDEN ISLANDS

EILEEN E. LANTRY

REVIEW AND HERALD®
PUBLISHING ASSOCIATION
Since 1861 | www.reviewandherald.com

Copyright © 2010 by Review and Herald® Publishing Association

Published by Review and Herald® Publishing Association, Hagerstown, MD 21741-1119

Review and Herald® titles may be purchased in bulk for educational, business, fundraising, or sales promotional use. For information, e-mail SpecialMarkets@reviewandherald.com.

The Review and Herald® Publishing Association publishes biblically based materials for spiritual, physical, and mental growth and Christian discipleship.

The author assumes full responsibility for the accuracy of all facts and quotations as cited in this book.

Unless otherwise noted, texts are from The New King James Version. Copyright © 1979, 1980, 1982 by Thomas Nelson, Inc. Used by permission. All rights reserved.

This book was
Edited by Penny Estes Wheeler
Designed by Ron J. Pride
Cover art by ©JupiterImages.com
Interior designed by Heather Rogers
Typeset: Bembo 11/13

PRINTED IN U.S.A.

14   13 12   11   10   5   4   3   2   1

Library of Congress Cataloging-in-Publication Data
Lantry, Eileen E.
  Broken stick : mission to the forbidden islands / Eileen E. Lantry.
     p. cm.
1. Missions—Solomon Islands. 2. Seventh-day Adventists—Missions—Solomon Islands. 3. Missionary stories 4. Ferris family. I. Title.
  BV3680.S6L36 2010
  286.7'9593—dc22

                                    2009037313

ISBN 978-0-8280-2069-5

DEDICATED TO

*The Skipper and the Engineer
of the Solomon Island Adventist Medical Ship, Maui (Light).*

*Their expertise, skill, dedication and Christlike love
blesses all who sail with them.*

Contents

THUNDER AND LIGHTNING

He stood totally camouflaged, peeking through the dense tropical forest vegetation.

Behind him, hidden on the high rock, crouched 40 to 50 of his warriors. Each held a war club and five-meter-long spears, each with sharp poisoned points made of black palm. Standing tall and strong, the leader watched, fierce anger burning within. How dare intruders violate their sacred beach! No stranger dared step on this special place, declared to be holy by the gods that ruled this island of Bellona in the Solomon Islands. And if they should dare, none lived to tell about it. With intense loyalty he would defend the domain of his hero gods—spirits controlled by the devil.

His keen eyes noted each man that climbed down the ship's ladder to the dinghy. He followed every stroke as they rowed silently to the shore then beached the dinghy and stepped on the sand. Slowly they walked toward the caves and hidden houses of the island gods within the caves.

This South Sea Island explorer and his sailors paused, glancing around to discern any sign of life. They did not see the man nor his well-camouflaged warriors who silently watched from the cliff overlooking the beach.

Then unable to contain his anger any longer, the leader let out a mighty yell. It reverberated against the volcanic cliffs like peals of thunder. The intruders froze in their tracks, feverishly looking around to see where the sound came from. In terror they saw the warrior leap off the overhanging rock followed in rapid sequence by his army. The warriors landed on the sand and yelling in concert, raced with clubs and spears to capture and kill the intruders.

To this South Sea explorer they seemed to come at him as fast and deadly as a flash of lightening. The frightened men turned and fled from the murderous charge. Reaching their dinghy just ahead of the mob, they shoved it into the surf and rowed furiously toward their boat. Close behind, the still raging warriors plunged into the waves, waving their clubs and throwing spears at the fleeing men.

Three days later the explorer entered Kopiu Bay on the open sea side of the large island of Guadalcanal. As his ship came closer he saw islanders that seemed to be working with a White man and woman. Two small White children played with several Black children. He anchored the ship and took a dinghy to shore.

The young man with dark curly hair stepped forward and extended his hand to the explorer. "Welcome to Kopiu village. I'm Norman Ferris, a missionary here on Guadalcanal. This is my wife, Ruby, and our children."

The traveler smiled. "That's a much different welcome than I received a few days ago when I landed on a small island about 90 miles southwest of here. I was nearly killed!"

"You must have stopped at the little island called Bellona," Norman told him. "I've heard a lot about these tall, strong, well-built Polynesian people. They don't let anyone come ashore. In fact, they maintain a direct communication with the devil and among many other things, he enables them to levitate."

The explorer nodded. Anything seemed possible with those frightening men.

"Using this supernatural power," Norman continued, "they rise and float in the air for short distances. Many of the bays around Bellona are dedicated to their gods, and fishing in the forbidden bays or even going near the caves and houses where their devil-gods are supposed to live means certain death."

"I believe it! Their chief warrior almost did us in! You can be sure I'll never go there again." Ending his terrifying story, the visitor added, "That island will always be off limits for me. I'm no match for the huge guy I call 'Thunder and Lightning.'"

After the man left Norman's thoughts constantly turned to the devil worshipers on Bellona and the nearby island of Rennell. He felt deep sympathy and compassion for the man the explorer labeled Thunder and Lightening, for his devoted warriors, and the people who lived there under the devil's control. Norman learned that the chief's actual name was Tiekika. He also learned that the Bellēnese claimed a voice that spoke through strange creatures demanded they attack and kill anyone who came near the dwelling places of their special gods.

Norman hated the way Satan manipulated the minds of these poor people.

The Bellonese and Rennellese are taller and stronger than the indigenous Solomon Islanders. The average Guadalcanalian seemed very *laissez faire* compared to the people from Bellona and Rennell who were much more warlike. Bellonese tribal chiefs were always male, whereas Guadalcanal society was more matriarchal and allowed women to own land and have the final say in many things.

Norman Ferris also knew that the government had passed a law to keep these two islands as an anthropological study site without contact with any outside influences. These restrictions affected all missionaries of all denominations who were forbidden to stay overnight on either island. Considering all these factors, how could he bring them the gospel of love and peace?

His concern deepened as he remembered Jesus' parting command, "Go... and make disciples of all the nations" (Matt. 28:19). Was God calling him to face these murderers? Should he try to get government permission to visit these islands? His mental turmoil heightened as he asked himself, "Does God want me to put my life in danger and possibly bring great sorrow to my wife and children?" Day after day he struggled with God in prayer, pleading, "Please God, show me Your will." Soon after, Norman received an answer. He felt that God spoke to him personally through 2 Timothy 1:7: "For God has not given us a spirit of fear, but of power and of love and of a sound mind."

That promise gave him peace. With it, he knew that he need not fear but trust the power of God's love. Now he could tell Ruby of his great burden.

That evening after the children slept he took her hand and said, "Ruby, let's talk a while. I need to share with you my struggle about the people of Bellona and Rennell."

Ruby listened thoughtfully and quietly. When he had voiced his convictions Norman paused a few moments to let her think, then asked, "Ruby, could God be asking me to be the one to open the way of the gospel of grace to these wonderful Polynesian people? They, too, must know that God's great plan of salvation by grace includes them. Remember the promise in Ephesians 2:6 that says that God raised us up with Christ and seated us with Him in heavenly places. Doesn't that 'us' include these wild, devil-controlled people?" he asked.

Ruby looked puzzled. "Are you saying that a man like Tiekika and his murderous warriors, by accepting God's grace, can someday sit with Jesus on thrones in heaven?"

Norman pointed to his Bible. "Why not? If God can save us, isn't His grace big enough to include them? I'll admit I don't completely comprehend verse 7 and the awesome meaning of the 'exceeding riches of hHis grace in His kindness toward us through Christ Jesus.' But I can believe that whatever God says, He does. God specializes in doing what to us humans seems impossible."

Ruby smiled. "I get what you mean." Her smile grew to a chuckle. "Can't you imagine those tall, fierce warriors of Bellona sitting humbly on thrones with Jesus, praising Him for the riches of His grace!"

They talked, prayed, and read more promises together. Then Ruby looked at him and said, "Norman, you will not go to Bellona alone. God will go before you. He'll be with you and never leave you. There's no need to be afraid."

Norman put his arms around her. "Let's give our all to Him again. Let's renew our dedication. Let's trust that God will use our surrender to open the way to bring His love to Bellona."

During the next few months Norman made favorable contact with Chief Tapongi of Rennell Island. Since no stranger could stay on that island overnight, the chief allowed Norman to take six of the island boys with him to learn to read and write. Among them was his son, Moa, who quickly learned the English language, learned to sing, and translated hymns into Renellese.

Norman felt the Holy Spirit's impression that the time had come to go to Bellona. First, he stopped at nearby Rennell Island to pick up his young friend, Moa, who had translated the song "Jesus Loves Me" into the Bellonese and Rennellese languages which are almost identical.

Evidently the village people at Bellona saw the ship far out at sea. In amazement they watched the ship anchor in one of the sacred bays. Immediately a crowd of villagers gathered on the high cliffs above the beach to see the strangers killed by their hero-god, for treading this holy ground would have meant death to even a Bellonese. In wonder their eyes followed as the White man with the boat's crew rowed ashore and landed on the sacred beach. Why did he gather them in a semicircle? Why did they stand and make that noise? They could understood the words, but what did "Jesus loves me" mean? Fear turned to anger. Were these strangers asking their god to do evil to them?

By this time Tiekika and his men had rushed to the rock above the sacred beach. Behind Tiekika, his faithful warriors crouched with spears and clubs. "No one will get away this time," he snarled. "Their heads will swing in our god's house very soon!"

Then he heard that strange noise. Never having heard singing, he muttered in a hoarse whisper, "They must be putting a curse on us!" The anger and hatred in his mind increased. His savage eyes watched the intruders' every move. He saw the man and his crew kneel down on the sand and bow their heads. He heard words he couldn't understand. Could they be praying to his devil gods?

When Norman rose from his knees he noticed an old man and some children farther down the beach, probably looking for clams. He turned to the crew. "You stay here and watch the dinghy," he told them. "I'll go alone to see if I can make contact with the people of this island. Maybe we'll be able to communicate."

He picked up his medical bag and a black book. Putting his hat back on his head, he started walking toward the old man, who seemed friendly. This led him further up the beach near the high rock.

Suddenly, a great yell thundered out across the bay. Norman looked up just in time to see a tall, muscular man leap from the rock followed by 40 or 50 warriors. They landed on their feet running swiftly toward him, spears held at the ready. Norman had no chance to run, nor any idea of running. With a glance skyward and a prayer to his heavenly Friend for wisdom and protection, the lone missionary knew he could face any situation.

Then he took off his hat and placed it on the sand. This, he knew, would be taken as a challenge by the heathen warriors surrounding him. It was a custom of the island people that drawing a line on the ground, or placing an object on the ground, constituted a challenge. With his hat on the sand, Norman stepped back a foot or two waiting for them. An attempt to flee would mean certain death.

Norman had come to Bellona to stand for God in whom he put his trust. He knew the devil fled before God's mighty power, so now he waited. Breathlessly, the crew and Moa watched with fear in their eyes. If Norman and God failed they too would die.

Thunder and Lightning, as swift as the name suggested, ran to the lone figure standing with nothing in his hands but a bag and a book. He stopped at the hat, accepting the challenge before him, while his warriors encircled the man. Thunder's murderous eyes looked directly into the eyes of the White man. But something seemed wrong! The man's brown eyes looked straight back at him with no sign of fear. Who could refuse to cower before him? Why did he not run in terror? Why did those eyes burn deeply into his?

Then Thunder's devilish rage took over. He reached past the hat, grabbed Norman's shirt and ripped it off his back. Next his strong hand clutched the white arm. Was he a devil spirit or a man? Tiekika squeezed the muscles until pain, like a searing torch, burned through Norman's body. Breathing a continuous prayer for great courage and faith, Norman waited—not for the death blow—but for God to act.

Then one of the watching older men shouted, "Let him live!"

Tiekika shouted back, "No. He dies!"

At that moment Tiekika seemed to feel a stronger arm take hold of his arm and with a twist of the wrist Tiekika felt power like a karate throw. To the surprise of both men, the muscular mighty warrior lost his balance and was thrown prostrate on the sand.

Had superhuman angelic power taken over? A shout and then laughter came from the people gathered on the hillside. Tiekika leaped to his feet, turned, and raced his fastest along the beach. His warriors followed. They vanished in the jungle.

Norman knew that when God sends an angel messenger, divine power wins over Satan. Standing alone, knowing he had been in the presence of a heavenly being, Norman felt cold chills creep up his spine and beads of perspiration ooze over his body. Immense relief overwhelmed him as he realized that God would continue to use His power to vanquish the enemy in the terrible controversy between Christ and Satan. God had won the first round in the battle. Victory would come on Bellona!

Norman beckoned toward the village people who waited on the cliff to come and gather around him and his crew. With Moa leading, they began singing "Jesus loves me this I know . . ." Slowly the village people came. With deep sympathy Norman noted the oozing sores and raw ugly ulcers on both adults and children, so opening his medicine bag he gave medical attention to the most needy. Then he motioned for them to join him kneeling in prayer. Moa translated his prayer: "O God, who made the heavens and the earth, I pray for Tiekeka, his warriors, and these dear village people, that they will know You love them. I pray they will believe in the mighty God whose power and strength is stronger than any warrior or devil god. Come to this island and bring peace and joy to each one, I pray in Jesus' name. Amen."

With that Norman turned to the boat with the promise, "We will come back."

BEGINNINGS, JOYS, AND TRIALS

Norman Ferris and his two brothers grew up on Lord Howe Island, 436 miles northeast of Sydney, Australia. The boys loved hearing their missionary parents tell Bible stories like Daniel in the Lion's Den and David and Goliath. They thrilled at each new story from their favorite mission field, the Solomon Islands. All three boys later declared that these daily worship stories influenced their life choices.

Early in life Norman committed his life to Jesus, remembering his father's words, "God had only one Son and He was a missionary."

At 19 Norman enrolled in the missionary course at Avondale College, in Cooranbong, Australia, with one purpose in mind—to serve God as a missionary in the Solomon Islands. In 1921 this scattered archipelago of mountainous islands and low-lying coral atolls northeast of Australia could only be reached by a steamer from Sydney, and depending on weather conditions, the voyage took two weeks to a month. Stretching about 900 miles in a southeasterly direction with six major Islands and about 992 smaller islands, atolls, and reefs, the Solomon Islands consist of thickly forested mountain ranges intersected by deep, narrow valleys.

Family and clan ties in the scattered small villages along the seacoast remain very strong. About 93 percent are Melanesians and 4 percent Polynesians who speak more than 80 different local languages plus 120 dialects. Communication is by "Solomon Island Pijin," a mixture of English and national dialects.

In the 1800s various Christian missions met to assign certain islands to different churches. Because of the missionaries' influence, a large percentage of the people in the Solomon Islands claim to be "Christians of a sort," but seldom had their lifestyle changed from heathen practices. However, this arrangement seemed compatible with their clan identity.

Thus most villages on one island claim to be Anglican while on another island the villages consist of Roman Catholics. Most of the larger islands became South Seas Evangelical, United Church, or Methodist, Baptist, Jehovah's Witness, and Assembly of God.. The different missions competed for territory. However, the committee did not assign any islands to the Seventh-day Adventists. So the early missionaries concluded that God wanted them to enter all the islands. This plan tended to create friction.

Despite knowing these challenges he would likely encounter, Norman's passion for missions grew daily. More and more he grasped God's miracle of salvation by grace. He understood that God will give this transforming power to even the wildest Solomon Islander. He visualized the promise in Ephesians 2:6, "made us sit together in the heavenly places in Christ Jesus," to include transformed devil worshipers sitting together on thrones with Christ beside the most dedicated missionaries. Norman truly believed that God's great love and saving grace included *all* His precious children. He longed to help them understand God's plan. To Norman, God's eternal plan offered everyone a relationship with God even closer than the angels have with Him.

In the missionary class at Avondale College, Norman's discerning eyes fastened on a vivacious girl, Ruby, who shared his love for God and missions. As often as possible they shared their dreams of seeing many of the Solomon Islanders accept the good news of salvation. When they finished the missionary course in 1923, their love for each other drew them together. The conference asked Norman to fill a vacancy as tent master for evangelistic meetings while Ruby worked at the Sydney Sanitarium. Then seeing Norman's dedication, the conference asked him to be part of the permanent staff after their marriage at the Concord Church in Sydney, on October 5, 1925.

In their first assignment, pastoring a small church, God blessed their zeal and they raised up a sizable church. The conference leaders noted their dedication for God, and at the end of 1926, invited them to go as missionaries to the Solomons.

While waiting a number of months for health clearances, they both attended classes on how to treat tropical diseases. At that time they felt restless to begin their missionary work in the Solomons and frustrated by how long they had to wait. But after they began their mission they realized that God had arranged that they spend extra time learning these valuable medical skills. This provided a key to showing their and God's love. With this ability they relieved many kinds of sicknesses plaguing the island people. God opened a door so they could use Jesus' methods of offering physical as well as spiritual healing.

On March 16, 1927, Norman and Ruby began their mission adventures in the Solomon Islands among the many villages of the Marovo Lagoon. The spectacular beauty of the Marovo Lagoon consists of a colorful expanse of calm water extending for 60 miles along the coast of the large island of New Georgia in the western province. Littered with myriad islets and atolls of living green, many are today inhabited with thriving villages asking for missionaries to come and teach them.

While they studied the language, in the mornings Norman taught through an interpreter at the Batuna Training School, supervising the school boys in the mission gardens and working in the sawmill in the afternoons. This mill produced the timber Norman used to build their first home. Construction took several months.

The Ferrises especially enjoyed the weekends when they left the station by canoe and visited the many villages along the lagoon. With their medical kit in hand, they visited each home.

After chatting a while they treated tropical ulcers, malaria, skin diseases, and other illnesses. Before leaving a home, they always prayed with the family. Thus they made friends for Jesus.

After a number of months living on New Georgia Island, Ruby became terribly sick. Malaria weakened her and quinine turned her once rosy cheeks yellow. Then she discovered she was pregnant. Since her intense sickness did not abate, the expectant parents prayed earnestly for wisdom and guidance from God. What did God want them to do—risk the baby's and Ruby's lives or return to Australia?

With his arms around his sweetheart, Norman prayed, "God, what shall we do? We don't want to be separated. We both love the people here. Please show us what is best for the mission work you gave us, and for the dear baby we already love."

The answer came when the mission leaders decided that for both her health and the expected baby, Ruby should return to Australia, and stay with her parents until the baby came. With tears, the sad couple parted. Ruby delivered a beautiful baby girl on January 15, 1928, at the Sydney Sanitarium. She named her Norma after her daddy.

When baby Norma was only a few months old, Ruby booked a steamer for Brisbane, and then on to the Solomon Islands. Even though she felt sapped of strength from her frequent bouts with malaria, she felt compelled to get back to the baby's daddy. Loss of sleep due to a colicky baby added to her tiredness. Two days later when they reached Brisbane, baby Norma developed a form of gastritis. Since they were in port all day, the worried mother contacted a doctor. After examining her, the doctor spoke kindly but firmly. "My dear new mother, you must not go to the tropics with this tiny, sick baby. She will die. Please do not go on!"

Ruby contacted the only woman she knew in Brisbane, who helped her find a friend who would take her in till she could notify her family in Sydney. Returning to the ship, she told the officers her problem. Without compassion, they dumped all her possessions, including a cot, tram, diapers, and much more on the wharf at 10:00 o'clock at night. Sick at heart, she watched the boat that would have taken her to the man she loved sail without her.

Ruby's sister, Mary, a trained nurse, secured passage on a boat that took passengers along Australia's coast. Soon she arrived in Brisbane to care for both the sick mother and baby. They returned together, and went straight to the Sydney Sanitarium. Even at the sanitarium baby Norma cried almost continually and slept poorly until Ruby became so worn out she could hardly function. After several weeks a pediatrician, Dr. Freeman, returned to the sanitarium from a graduate course on infant care he'd taken in Ireland. She immediately took baby Norma off the prescribed diet and put her on strained granose gruel, a whole grain cooked cereal. Within days Norma changed—no more diarrhea, better sleep, and a happy baby. Over the next few weeks little Norma thrived on whole granose with milk. Obviously she had become allergic to the other diet.

Now hoping to sail soon, Ruby took her baby for a final check-up. The doctor warned, "You have a beautiful, healthy baby now. However, I cannot allow you to take her to the tropics for a couple of years."

Filled with despair and disappointment she wrote out the problem to Norman. He answered her pleading letter. "My dear Ruby, I feel so sad for you, but I'm happy little Norma is doing so well. You will have to decide between two difficult alternatives. First, leave the baby with your sister, Mary, and return to me until our next furlough. Second, if you cannot part with our precious baby, I must postpone our mission work here and return to my dear family. I fully understand your problem, but I do not feel it is right for me to tell you what to do. You will have to make the decision. I love you and will be praying that you will do God's will. Love, Norman."

Ruby held her beautiful curly-haired child and wept in anguish. "Help me, God! Please show me Your will. Should I leave my dear baby, or should I go back to the tropics and serve You there with my husband? How can I leave my precious baby?"

Suddenly a Bible text hit her mind with full force. "He who loves father or mother more than Me is not worthy of Me. And he who loves son or daughter more than Me is not worthy of Me. And he who does not take his cross and follow after Me is not worthy of Me" (Matt. 10:37, 38).

With intense struggle, Ruby chose to take up her cross and leave her precious little Norma. She knew she could not find a better person to care for her than her sister, Mary.

Ruby's heart nearly broke as the steamer pulled out from the wharf. But she felt peace in knowing a mother's love can be selfish if it stands in the way of serving God and her child's best good. Her sacrifice seemed small considering that God gave His only Son to the human race forever. She felt an urgency to join Norman in bringing salvation to people living in heathen darkness who, if they accepted His love, could someday be closer than angels sitting with God on His throne.

Overjoyed to have her back after months of separation, Norman gladly turned the home duties back to her. Between the tasks of helping Norman with mission work, she made pretty dresses to send to Norma, often thinking of Hannah in the Bible who made coats for her son, Samuel. With joy she thanked God for the little house Norman had completely built from the timber at the mill while she was in Australia.

Hardly had the paint dried on their new house, when the mission committee asked them to transfer to the island of Vella Lavella, a smaller island in the New Georgia group northeast of Batuna. They'd live at a village called Dovelle. Why were they needed there? The request read, "You must take the place of the Lee family, who just lost their little boy, Noel, due to sickness. Mr. and Mrs. Lee returned to Australia."

Upon arrival at Dovelle, Ruby and Norman immediately understood why little Noel had died. They loved the friendly nationals, but hated the filth in the village. Their house, made of native material with an iron roof and board flooring, had a detached kitchen. The water supply, collected from an iron tank on the roof, made an ideal breeding place for anopheles mosquitoes. Not only did mosquitoes abound, but flies swarmed everywhere, feeding on human excreta in the surrounding bush. They encountered snakes and centipedes in unexpected places. Their challenge: how could they teach these dear people clean living? If only they would listen, and follow practical simple hygiene, they could prevent most of their diseases.

Since no roads penetrated the deep jungle and steep mountains, Norman enjoyed taking Ruby around their island parish in a boat, visiting each home in the villages. On one trip they discovered Nellie and Norman Watkins whom they had met as fellow passengers on the steamer when they first came to the Solomons. Norman Watkins managed a copra plantation which exported this dried coconut product.

On that visit friendly Nellie gave Ruby a broad smile and said, "Ruby, I see you're expecting a second baby. You know the Methodist Hospital is a clean facility with a good doctor. And it operates at Munda only five miles from here. Would you like to stay with us when your baby comes due?"

"That would be a great blessing! Thanks so much. We'll take you up on your offer." Ruby smiled with gratitude.

Some months later while visiting around their parish, they anchored their boat at the plantation's wharf a week or so before they expected the baby. As they arrived after sunset, they decided to sleep on the boat overnight and move into the Watkins home the next morning. Tired from the trip, Norman and Ruby went to bed early. About 10:00 o'clock Ruby awakened Norman.

"The baby's on its way! Let's go now!"

Norman awakened the engine boy. "Hurry! We must go to the hospital immediately."

Time and time again the boy tried, but the engine would not turn over. Feeling desperate, Norman jumped from the deck and ran to the Watkins home.

Hearing the words, "Ruby's in labor" they sprang into action. Soon all four crowded into an outboard dingy, covering the five miles to Munda in record time. Spasms of pain told Ruby her baby was well on the way.

Greatly relieved to be at the hospital, Norman followed the nurse and Ruby to her room. In no time a healthy baby boy lay crying lustily on the bed. Overjoyed, Norman saw his first son, whom they named Raymond Harrison.

Soon after Ray's birth, word came through that a strong cyclone had taken off the roof of the Dovelle Mission house. Knowing the structure wasn't worth repairing and they couldn't return to that area with a new baby, Norman took the boat and packed up what few belongings he could find. Since New Georgia Island was not far, they went back to the Batuna School, visiting the believers at Lavella frequently.

Since the Batuna area had no home in which the Ferris family could live, the mission president suggested that Ruby and the baby return to Australia. "With your furlough only a few months away," he told Norman, "you will be following them soon." This they did.

On the long trip back to Sydney, Ruby prayed often and earnestly that Norma would accept her as her mother. With joy she thrilled at the sight of her robust, but shy little daughter. Little Norma looked quizzically at this new person. Mary took her little hand, and led her to Ruby repeating, "Mother, your mother." Only a short time went by until love broke through. Little Norma slowly came to her and lifted up her hands. Ruby praised God as Norma snuggled up to her. What joy to have her little girl in her arms!

But continual high temperatures and days in bed suffering from the periodic chills and fever of malaria left Ruby weak and anemic. Gradually she became unable to sustain baby Ray with breast milk. Week after week, he failed to gain weight. When he grew old enough, granose gruel made a big difference. Soon his big blue eyes brightened and rosy cheeks made him an adorable baby.

The day finally arrived when a letter came from Norman. "I'm coming to Australia via New Hebrides, and will dock at my parents' home before coming to Sydney," he wrote. "Since it is more than 400 miles northeast of Sydney, would you and the children please take the steamer to meet me at Lord Howe Island?"

What a great reunion when his boat arrived! Norma, nearing her third birthday, looked suspiciously at her daddy. He began to play with her using balloons and a soft rubber ball. Hide and seek proved lots of fun too. Very soon his love and affection won her over. What joy filled Norman's heart as he held both Norma and little Ray, now 8 months old.

Glorious family togetherness, playing with the children, enjoying picnics at the beach and sharing God's blessings with the grandparents filled their cup of joy! Now Norman could tell his parents mission stories of God's leading and power, just like they used to read Solomon Island stories to him and his brothers when he was a child.

Broken Stick

The rest of the three months furlough raced by visiting with Ruby's parents in Sydney. Too soon the missionary family of four boarded the steamer that would take them back to the Solomons. But Satan had a sinister plan to destroy this happiness.

BABY OVERBOARD

Relaxing on deck chairs as they watched the children play, Norman explained the travel plans to Ruby. "After several weeks on the open sea, we'll dock at the closest port of call on the island of Rendova, in the New Georgia group. The small interisland mission boat, *Kima,* will take us on to Marovo Lagoon, in New Georgia Island."

When they landed at Rendova, they found the *Kima* anchored for the night. High winds whipped its sails and heavy seas thwarted any plans to leave that evening. As the Ferris family boarded the *Kima* they discovered the boat filled with nationals and their gear, also going to Marovo.

Hoping the morning would bring calmer waters, Norman explained to Ruby, "Sorry, honey, but there's no space left on the deck. We'll have to stretch out on the cabin roof top without any mattresses."

Morning brought no change in the weather. Since the closest way would take them through heavy seas, the captain chose the safest way. That meant traveling all day long via the northern tip of New Georgia Island, before they could turn south and enter the lagoon. Because the ship rolled and tossed almost uncontrollably, the crew put up sails to steady the boat.

Norman watched his good friend, Kata Rangoso, a handsome, broad-shouldered giant of a man, at the wheel. Rangoso, the son of a headhunter chief, became a Christian at age 15. His brilliant mind soon grasped principles of leadership that only God through his study of the Bible could teach him. By 1930 Rangoso's humble yet dignified manner, plus his faithfulness, endeared him to the people in the western Solomons. Often Norman had traveled with him. As captain of the little ship he guided the boat with care. The prow of the boat hit every wave with a thud while the passengers held on to whatever they could.

A crew member remarked to Norman, "I'm glad he's captain of this boat! Notice his unusual skill in rough waters." Then he added, "I wish we could have entered the lagoon by the shorter way with which we're more familiar. Yet I'm confident he'll take great care as he pilots this boat through this narrow and dangerous entrance into the lagoon."

Frequently Rangoso gave the Ferrises a broad, ready grin of assurance.

Late that night they entered the calm waters of the Marovo Lagoon. "What a relief after so many hours of pounding the waves and being tossed by the stormy sea! I'm exhausted and hungry," exclaimed Ruby.

"No chance to get to our food in this crowded boat. I hope we'll soon land. Since this is the largest lagoon in the world, it may take awhile." Norman noticed her yawn and added, "My dear, now that we're in calm waters, why don't you take advantage of the cool sea breeze and rest up there on the cabin rooftop? I'll enjoy watching Rangoso flash his beam of light across the mirror surface of the waters searching for landmarks. Perhaps I can learn for the future."

"Are you sure it's safe?" asked Ruby.

"He's sailed these waters in canoes and mission vessels for years. It's my guess he knows about every submerged rock in this lagoon plus all the safe channels."

Relieved and content, Ruby climbed to the roof, and lay down. Norman handed her little Norma on her left side and baby Ray on her right arm. Feeling secure, she quickly fell asleep. Meanwhile Norman watched closely as Rangoso constantly checked his charts and scanned the waters with his light.

With sudden violence the *Kima* lurched over to the port side. Without even sighting a ripple in the water the boat had struck an uncharted submerged rock. Everything loose on the deck slid into the water, including the missionaries' belongings. Rangoso tried desperately to bring the boat to an upright position, but the keel had run into a groove in the rock and it held her fast. The impact catapulted the relaxed little Norma into the sea. Immediately her frantic mother screamed, "Norma fell overboard! Quick! Quick! She's in the water!"

Terrible fear overwhelmed Ruby. Memories of almost losing Norma when she was a baby flooded her mind, but the memory of how God used people to bring healing to her little body brought hope now.

Jimaru, Rangoso's brother and another crewman quickly dived overboard. He came up with only a basket of sweet potatoes. Instantly Rangoso dived deep into the lagoon searching frantically among the treacherous coral. Clutching her baby boy, Ruby cried and prayed softly while Norman prayed aloud. Rangoso bobbed to the surface for a deep breath, and again disappeared into the deep gloom. Norman, not a good swimmer like the nationals, held his wife and baby on the dangerous tilting roof, anxiously watching the beam of a flashlight that swept over the water.

Rangoso stretched out his hands this way and that, praying, "Please, God, help me find the little girl." His hands touched a basket that had fallen from the deck, then a weed-covered stone. He turned and felt something soft— clothes, hair. Then placing little Norma on his shoulders, he gave a powerful kick on the coral on the sea bottom, unconcerned that it might cut his tough bare feet. A moment later he placed Norma in her father's arms. Turning her upside down, Norman gently shook the water out of her, and she began to cry.

What a welcome sound that was! "Thank you God and Rangoso," the grateful mother prayed. "She seems none the worse for her bath. Thank you so very much!"

Someone yelled orders. "Everyone go forward, and see if by going astern quickly the weight will shift and together we can get the boat off the rock."

Norman hurried to assist Ruby and the baby. As they reached the center of the boat, it suddenly turned throwing all three of them and many others into the water on the starboard side. Crew members quickly jumped to their aide and helped them back on board. With the receding tide the ship's position was becoming precarious, and the small, leaky dingy they towed could not possibly be of much help for survival.

Rangoso chose two crewmen, telling them, "Please take the dingy and get help from the nearest village. It could be miles away."

They disappeared in the darkness. Anxious hours passed as the *Kima* slowly sank further and further into the sea. The women sat on the stern like ducks ready to dive into the water. They waited, prayed, and listened in the dark. After what seemed like hours they heard the noise of the paddles of a Man o'War canoe. Immediately many prayers went heavenward thanking God for hearing and answering their pleas for help.

Rangoso put all the women and children into the canoe. The village men took them to an uninhabited island about half an hour from the shipwreck.

Broken Stick

Ruby hardly noticed that she had no food, but without shelter they became bait for swarms of mosquitoes. Two little heads lay resting on her lap. Thankful for both of her children, she looked at the bright stars thickly scattered like jewels overhead. They reminded her of a Bible verse that described Rangoso's life: "They that be wise shall shine as the brightness of the firmament; and they that turn many to righteousness as the stars for ever and ever" (Dan. 12:3, KJV). As he dived three times to save Norma, Ruby knew that Rangoso devoted all his energies turning his people to God's love. Her heart filled with joy as she watched the first streaks of dawn culminate in a glorious sunrise. Ruby envisioned this heathen boy who grew up in darkness and fear. Now a transformed leader, his life shown brighter than the rising sun. *Yes,* Ruby thought, *one day Rangoso will sit with God on a special throne reigning with Him.*

The canoe arrived about 9:00 o'clock that morning. Norman had asked one of the men from the village to take a tin of Weet-Bix to Ruby and the waiting women and children. Norman and Ruby had brought it from Australia. As she shared these nutritious breakfast biscuits, Ruby thought, *Just like my dear husband, thinking of others. He remembered we'd had no food since the day before.*

Around 3:00 p.m. the full tide came in. With extra help from the village men the boat floated once more. They found no damage except a little piece of lost copper from the keel. Late the next morning they arrived at the school in Batuna, worn and weary. The Ferris family felt thankful for temporary accommodations in one of the mission staff houses.

A week later the Mission Committee sent word to Norman and Ruby. "Would you be willing to join Jugha and start a mission on the big island of Guadalcanal? Jugha is pioneering alone, and the challenge of working alone among the devil worshipers has become too much for him. He needs your help."

"Jugha has an interesting story," Norman explained to Ruby. "Kata Rangoso's father captured Jugha in a successful headhunting raid. His father was the chief of a village on the Marovo Lagoon, and he planned to offer the boy as a sacrifice, a burnt offering, in his devil worship. It was a horrible custom used to express gratitude for victory.

"However, during the intervening time before he would sacrifice the boy, the chief saw potential in him and decided to adopt him as his own son. He allowed Jugha to go to the mission school with Kata Rangoso and together they gave their hearts to Jesus. He and Kata were baptized in 1918. Jugha has dedicated his life to sharing his love for Jesus. I'm sure we'll enjoy teaming up with him."

At the suggestion of the mission leader, Norman loaded the mission launch, *Melanesia*, with building materials and tools. His first assignment—to erect a small two-roomed shelter, a home for his family, on a piece of donated ground at Wanderer Bay in Guadalcanal. Ruby stayed with the children while Norman and the boat crew worked to build the temporary house.

Though separated, both Ruby and Norman prayed that the Holy Spirit would teach them how to make Jesus attractive to these heathen people. Would they exchange their cruelty, fear, and hate for peace, love, hope, and joy? From a lifetime of devil worship, could they desire a God who cared enough to die for them? Remembering how God had solved many problems and difficulties for them during the past seven years, they found courage that His grace has no limit.

But Norman shook his head as he studied the property given to the mission. A steep hill extended almost to the shore of Wanderer's Bay. He must build the house on that almost vertical slope with the back door level with the ground. The front part, resting on huge logs, must be high enough for the boat's crew to live underneath. The small kitchen would look like an alcove.

Below him the village homes dotted the shore. Legally, each family belonged to either the Church of England or the Catholic mission. In practice and lifestyle the villagers lived in filth and heathenism. In their ignorance they followed without question the commands of their priests. Already Norman saw evidence that these simple people would have nothing to do with this new missionary.

Night after night Norman went to sleep praying, "Heavenly Father, give us wisdom, tact, and love to know how to reach these precious people You have called us to serve. Show us how to start."

BREAKTHROUGH

When Norman finished the temporary two-room shelter at Wanderer's Bay, he returned for Ruby and the children. They loaded all their belongings in the *Melanesia* and arrived in a terrible storm. It was 1932. The villagers eyed them suspiciously and refused to allow the newcomers to barter for fresh food for themselves or the boat crew.

At night the mosquitoes swarmed over them until Norman devised the idea of burning wet chips and smoking them out. However, they rejoiced to discover that in spite of the constant bites, malaria was practically nonexistent in that region. Their health greatly improved as long as they stayed near the Bay.

Since their home perched on the side of a mountain, on rainy days they slipped and slid down the muddy trail to the village below. However, a short government road ran right through the middle of the village, free to all. Since little Norma and Ray loved these walks, Norman and Ruby took them often, hoping to make friends. Continually they pleaded, "God give us a breakthrough. All the people consider us imposters."

One morning as Norman worked at putting up a tank to improve their water supply, a man climbed up the path to him. Norman asked in pigeon English, "What name you come?" meaning, "What brought you up here?"

He answered, "Mary belong me sick too much. More better Mary belong you come look 'im."

Norman called Ruby, "This man's wife is sick and he wants you [Mary belong you—Ruby] to go down and see what you can do to help her."

By questioning him, Ruby found out that Lizzie, his wife had been in labor for a day or so. The baby had been born, but Lizzie retained the placenta. For two or three days they had heard cries in the bush. Now they knew why.

Ruby quickly put hot water in a bucket. Taking her medical kit she followed Mechael to the place of confinement. She was dumfounded to see Lizzie lying on the cold ground without any covering, semiconscious. She recognized Mechael as the schoolteacher in the Church of England village. Why, she wondered, had he come to them when the village felt so biased against them.

After a few manipulations the afterbirth came out without any complications. Knowing the native custom that women are not allowed back in the village after giving birth for at least seven days, and sometimes two weeks, Ruby suggested something that was strictly taboo. "Lizzie, she die. You take 'm to warm house. Need cover."

Mechael conceded to Ruby's request. Now baby and mother could be on their way to health again. The next day Norman looked down the hill in surprise. "Come, Ruby!" he called. "Look at the stream of women climbing up our mountain path loaded with baskets full of food. Let's go to meet them."

Full of smiles, they explained in pigeon English, "Lizzie, she live. Pickininny eat."

What a thank offering for saving a mother and her baby! Gratefully the missionaries accepted the food as the women placed it in their makeshift kitchen. After they left, the happy couple gathered their children around them and knelt in prayer. "Thank you, God. You provided a way to break through the barrier so we can make friends in this village. Please send Your angels to help them understand God's plan, that they shall receive His everlasting kingdom." From that day on the village people came to be treated for their many sicknesses. The missionaries gave injections, bound up sores, and helped whenever called upon. The unity of love formed a firm bond between them. The boat crew joined them as they walked down the road to the Catholic mission station. Visiting each home, the crew, in their language, told Bible stories of Jesus to eager children and their parents.

The priest was losing the confidence of the people so he devised a clever plan. He would convince the ignorant people that his power exceeded that of the White missionary. To prove his claims, he told the people he could cause the blood of Christ to fall down from heaven. This would fall on all who came and knelt to receive forgiveness of sin.

Previously, the priest had arranged for a native boy to hide in the ceiling of the church with a freshly beheaded cock. At just the right moment he would squeeze the cock over a small hole and the blood would flow. It worked for a few moments, and people were convinced. Then the boy's voice came strong and clear. "Blood belong this cockarako dry up-finish. More better you kill 'm one more cock." [The blood from this rooster is dried up. You need to kill one more cock.]

Because of the priest's deception, he lost his influence. God turned this lie to His glory. The Catholic members came to Norman requesting a teacher for their children. Pleased, Norman praised God for the joy of placing a capable Adventist national in that village.

Every Sabbath morning the crew and the missionaries gathered for Sabbath school under their house. One Sabbath, during the song, a tall strong man came stomping up the path and demanded, "Me want im pump. Picanniny belong me sick too much." No doubt he had seen the missionaries using a large syringe to wash the infection out of ulcers and thought it would draw the problem from his baby's body.

Norman explained in Pijin, "We never loan our medical things to anyone. After 'lotu' [worship] we will come to your village to see your sick child."

Worship ended and Norman and Ruby took the medical kit to this heathen village where pigs, dogs, and people all lived together. They discovered an 18-month-old girl who had not had a bowel movement for three days. She was crying hard, as if in pain. Ruby began to prepare a mixture that would soon bring relief. But before she could give it to the child, the mother and whole family fled in fear to the bush refusing to let Ruby get near them. Only one person in the village would allow Norman to help her with an injection, a woman suffering from an ugly tropical ulcer with blood running from it and flies swarming over it. Sadly they walked home praying, "We could have easily cured the girl's constipation. Please God, show us how to gain the confidence of these dear heathen people."

The next morning Ruby hurried to the home of the sick child. In horror, she staggered at the sight! The devil priest had cut a gash an inch deep around the buttocks of the tiny girl from one side of the anus to the other. The little girl lay semiconscious. The father turned to Ruby and told her why he permitted the devil priest to cut his baby. It was to, "Let devil out!" The devil priest frowned as he watched Ruby make a dressing of soothing ointment over the deep cut, saying over and over in Pijin, "How could you do such a foolish thing?"

Sternly she turned to the devil priest, struggling to control her anger. "I shall report you to the government for this horrible deed. This baby will surely die."

The next morning as they approached the village, they heard cries of mourning. The mother sat on a wooden slat bed holding the little body. Ruby sat beside her, put her arms around her and cried, "I'm so sorry, so sorry. How many other children do you have?"

Choking with grief the poor mother replied, "This make im four fellow he die finish." Ruby's heart broke as she thought of her own two children, snug and happy at home, compared to this poor heathen mother who had lost all four of hers, through ignorance. How Jesus must grieve when these dear people refuse the healing power of the gospel of Christ, that would give them life, health, peace, and joy!

Shortly after this Norman had a severe attack of sharp pain, which didn't respond to treatment. (It was probably kidney stones.) The pain became so severe that Ruby feared they might have to bury him on this lonely outpost. The crew and teachers prayed for him as they made the boat ready to take him to the nearest hospital at Tulagi, in the Florida Islands, more than 10 hours away. They started out, but heavy seas made the going hard so they took shelter off a small island for the night. When they arrived at the port the next morning, the doctors told them that the steamer *Malaita* was due the next day, en route to Sydney. "You need professional medical help," he told Norman. "You need to be on that boat." In severe pain, Norman agreed.

And so Norman boarded the steamer for Sydney, and the boat crew took Ruby and the children back to Wanderer Bay. These loyal Christian nationals faithfully cared for and protected the little family until Norman returned, completely well, six long weeks later.

About this time the mission committee realized this area of Guadalcanal needed a training school for future workers. Norman began searching for adequate land and eventually he approached the government officer with this request. "Sir, we want to build a school for the people in this area. I have found a very suitable tract of level land on Kopiu Bay consisting of more than 360 acres. This property is located about six miles up the coast from Marau Sound. I would like to sign a 99-year lease." After investigation, they granted the lease and Norman signed the proper papers. The owner, a chief, put his thumbprint beside Norman's signature making all things legal to build a school.

Their leaving Wanderer's Bay brought sorrow to the dear people they loved so much. Ruby never forgot the little mother who had lost all four children, clinging to her crying, "Mama, Mama, what will we do when you go?" Not many in the Catholic village chose to change their thinking and worship, but Ruby and this sad mother parted as dear friends.

Norman praised God for this shift to a more suitable area. The growing mission desperately needed more teachers. With the help of local people, he began to clear the jungle growing near the water's edge. First, Norman erected a temporary two-room shelter out of jungle material on the beach. It had bamboo walls and a thatched leaf roof. He split sago palms for the floor. Near the lean-to kitchen outside, he placed two large stones where Ruby could cook her delightful meals over the fire that burned between them. When they moved to this home near the boat anchorage, the children squealed in delight. Now they could play all day in the water, with Ruby watching as she worked.

The new location had both advantages and disadvantages. Their only bathing and washing facility was a lice-infected mountain stream. While Mama Ruby carried the clothes up to the creek, scrubbed the laundry on rocks, and dried it over the bushes, the children loved trying to paddle in the round galvanized wash tub she had used.

Under God's blessings the mission property at Kopiu proved to be productive. Gardens flourished. Norman laid plans for future buildings. A contractor builder from Sydney, Mr. Richardson, came to build a permanent worker's home on the hill. Meanwhile Norman began work on substantial buildings made from native material for the mission station—at first a church, then a school, and later dormitories for the students. To start school as soon as possible, the church served as a temporary school room during the week.

After years of living in crude structures, the Ferris family rejoiced at the comfort of their well-built new home. However, the new place bred many malaria mosquitoes. Again the family must fight this wretched disease with nasty, bitter quinine tablets, which the children hated.

They rejoiced when Norman secured two bulls, Buck and Bill. The children enjoyed watching them plough the fields, help with road building, and with transporting goods from the shore up to the new mission station on the hill.

Word spread to surrounding villages that the sick could find help at the Kopiu station. Norman ran his clinic under the house, which became a hospital and medical center, and medical work soon became the center of his outreach to the people. Long lines of hurting humanity walked or hobbled single file up the pathway to their house. Here, surrounded by the bright flowers Ruby had planted, they sat quietly on the lawn waiting their turn for treatment and hope. Norman sat on a box attending their needs by the hour. He treated malaria, dysentery, tuberculosis, leprosy, ulcers, and yaws (a severe tropical ulcer), aching teeth, and abscesses. Ruby helped with the maternity cases.

On his monthly 10-hour trips to Tulagi Norman brought back mail, household supplies, and medicines and other items which he secured from the hospital. This provided for not only their needs, but also those of their nearest neighbors at the Catholic Mission, and missionaries of other faiths who didn't have boats. In appreciation the Catholic Brothers gave the Ferris family a milk cow. They taught a boy how to milk the cow morning and evening. With fresh milk, chickens for eggs, bananas and other fruits, plus fresh vegetables from the garden, the family, the boat crew, plus teachers, and students were almost self-contained.

Norman, a master carpenter, shared his talents with the nationals. Norma and Ray loved playing in the shavings from the timber that the men turned into tables, chairs, dressing tables, beds, bookcases, and so on. Norman built all the furniture they owned. By 1933 the Kopiu school was filled with eager students and dedicated teachers. Under God's blessings the Kopiu mission prospered, bringing the light of God's love to many villages.

But the surrounding villages, who had used the property for their gardens, refused to relinquish their hold. Turning to God for help, Norman prayed, "Precious Lord, this is Your mission. Please solve our problems and remove our difficulties by your power."

Fortunately, the government had given a copy of the lease to one of the head chiefs. He brought it out to show the troublemakers, pointing to Norman Ferris' signature and his own thumbprint. This proved that the Seventh-day Adventist Mission had a legal right to continue to claim the land. God always has ways to solve difficulties if we ask Him.

With all his many responsibilities, at heart Norman's greatest desire was to be like Jesus, a pastor shepherd. He constantly asked for wisdom, tact, and power to know how to make contact with a heathen village so he did not offend their customs and ways. First, he always contacted the chief. Then he'd visit each thatch house to get acquainted with the men. He tried to talk with the women and children but often fear of a White man made them run screaming into the bush.

Almost every Sabbath afternoon the Ferris family enjoyed their usual weekly afternoon walk from village to village along the coast. They often walked for miles. Little Norma and Ray pretended to be missionaries like Daddy and Mother, visiting the people. How important they felt when Daddy let them carry his medical kit and Bible. Norman stopped at each home, giving injections where necessary. In each humble hut, he prayed with the people. The children watched the faces of the elderly, the blind, and infirm. They saw the happy smiles of joy when their daddy placed his hands on each one in prayer. Never before had these simple people experienced a pastor shepherd who loved them from the heart. No longer strangers, they felt accepted and blessed by the missionary family's visit.

In the various classes Norman taught in the mission school, he used every opportunity to blend faith and learning. His heart thrilled as his students joined him in a closer love relationship with Jesus. He challenged them to grasp that God included them in Psalms 8:5: "You have made him [mankind] a little lower than the angels." The eyes of the boys and girls grew wide in wonder as they understood God's larger plan. What joy it is that someday in heaven, saved by Jesus' grace, they, the youth of the Solomon Islands, shall be even closer in a love relationship with God than the angels who have never fallen!

Norman praised God as he saw that these youth from Kopiu School would soon serve as leaders to bring the gospel of God's love to their villages and tribes.

5

NGHATA, THE DEVIL PRIEST

Once the Kopiu Station became established, Norman extended his gospel ministry to other villages. He traveled on the mission ship *Marara* along the coast on the "weather side" of Guadalcanal. Here violent storms frequently came in from the sea.

Ruby and the children often went with him. Thrilled, young Norma and Ray sat one on each side of their competent sea captain father so they could watch his strong hands control the wheel. They squealed in glee when waves from the rough sea washed over the bow of the ship. But when the crashing waves became too high and rough for safety, Dad would have one of the crew take the children to the cabin below deck.

The first thing Norman did at each village was to set up a medical clinic. Sitting on a box, he treated the physical needs of every person who came to him. When all had been helped he asked them to sit down on the grass and he told them gospel stories of Jesus' love using a Sabbath School Picture Roll. Ruby used this ideal time to continue their children's home schooling. While their father treated the sick, weather permitting, Ruby took Norma and Ray down to the beach. There by the clear water and often gentle waves, she had guided their correspondence school work. Curious village children often came close to eagerly listen in.

On October 17, 1932, the Ferris family started a special trip to Tulagi, the capital on the nearby Florida Islands. Their destination: the only hospital in the area. Norma and Ray and the children shared the excitement that Ruby would give birth to their third child, due in a few days.

This trip took them through the beautiful Marau Sound. They loved this place. On one side the sound is bordered by mountains that sweep down to the mangrove lined shore, the habitat of many crocodiles. On the seaward side, graceful coconut trees filled the islands that made up the sound.

Norman's passion to bring the gospel to the hundreds of villages along the coast continually grew. Often as the mission ship sailed through the sound, the crews gathered for worship. Their harmonious songs vibrated over the waters toward the villages. Norman pleaded, "Lord, please open our work in these villages so that each one who lives there may choose to accept Jesus' invitation to live with Him eternally."

As the boat passed village after village along the coast, they watched the smoke from hundreds of fires rising against the blue sky. In one village especially near the coast Norman's attention was caught by an exceptionally large tree. How he longed to go there to the village near it with the gospel. Little did he realize how quickly his prayer would be answered.

The *Marara* tied up at the wharf in Tulagi. Their journey from Kopiu to Tulagi had taken most of the day. The sun was low in the sky when the crew gathered on the bow of the ship to begin their evening worship. As usual, their harmonious voices echoed over the port and many villagers stopped to listen to the words of the hymns.

Early the next morning, before the day's activities began, the sweet sound of the crew singing gospel songs again reverberated over the waters. After the singing Norman prayed, pleading with God to send the Holy Spirit to open the way to unentered villages in Guadalcanal. Unknown to Norman and the crew, while they were having morning and evening worship, a lone man hid in the shadows of the surrounding trees near the wharf. For two days, evening and morning, he came to listen to the singing. On the morning of the third day, October 20, the man could contain his curiosity no longer. Shyly, carefully, he walked to the wharf and approached Norman with this request. "Please, Masta, [the greeting of respect] can you come to my village? Will you teach my people to sing?"

"Where is your village?"

The chief pointed across the waters to the island of Guadalcanal. "See that big tree? I'm the chief of that village. Its name is Koilotumaria. My name is Kaomane Mau."

Norman's heart skipped a beat. "Yes, I would be glad to come to your village," he told the man. "Please wait here. I will come back soon."

Norman hurried to make arrangements with the resident doctor for

Ruby and the children to be cared for while he was away. Then with the chief on board, they set sail for the village of Koilotumaria located on the calm side of the coast of Guadalcanal. As he guided the ship, Norman continually thanked God for the opportunity to enter this first village on the leeward side of the island with the gospel. Music, with God's blessing, had opened the door!

Norman and the crew waited while chief Kaomane Mau disembarked to prepare the people for the arrival of a White man. Sadly, they were still haunted by memories of White slave traders who had stolen their children. Their hearts remained filled with fear, distrust, and hatred for White men.

Upon the chief's return, he beckoned from his canoe. "Come." Eagerly the missionary, his crew, and the cook boy, Imbi, went ashore. Right away they began to teach the villagers hymns and choruses. They also hung their Picture Rolls on trees and told them stories of Jesus.

But they knew nothing of Nghata! He ruled as the paramount devil priest of all the villages on the east coast of Guadalcanal. Busy with his early morning rituals, he checked all the tokens of his power in his little bag. The bone. The head of a chicken. Its blood and entrails. Yes, now he could begin his incantations. Suddenly, the devil appeared to him with a special message.

"Nghata, today a White man came to Koilotumaria. He is dangerous! He will bring disharmony to our people. You must take your sword. Go soon and kill him."

Following the chanting of his incantations, Nghata took his black ebony sword. Already several chips notched the sword's handle. Each chip represented a ceremonial murder Nghata had done at the devil's command. Nghata left immediately for he must walk several hours from his village, Tenabui, to Koilotumaria. But his steps were sure. His mind made up. He was on a mission.

No one saw him enter the village. No one saw him slip behind a bush where he stood listening to the singing. As they sang, "Jesus loves me" the devil filled his heart with hate and fury at Jesus' name. Nghata heard both the White men and his native crew telling the villagers stories of Jesus and healing miracles of His love. The villagers listened spellbound.

Suddenly the horrific power of Satan took over Nghata. With a mighty yell, he interrupted the storyteller. His sword held high, completely devil-possessed, he rushed toward Norman to kill him. He was wild with anger, consumed by hatred, demonic fury, and strength. Only a few steps separated them when Norman quickly prayed, "Dear God, send Your mighty arm of power." That prayer stopped Nghata in his tracks. He literally could not move. An aura of power surrounded the White man that he could not penetrate. Instinctively Nghata knew he faced a force far greater than that of Satan.

Several strong men in the crowd rushed forward, grabbed Nghata, and took his sword from him. Now he was able to move again, and with him kicking, fighting, and screaming the men dragged him away.

For three days the missionary and his crew stayed in the village. Word spread to surrounding villages. More and more people came to listen to the singing. Best of all they heard about a Mighty Warrior called Jesus, stronger even than the devil priest. Could this Jesus really bring peace and safety with no more headhunting and fighting?

On the morning of the third day, Norman approached the chief with the news that it was time for him to leave.

The chief was not ready to let him go. "Please stay and teach the people to sing and tell more stories from God's book about the pictures," he pleaded.

"I'm sorry," Norman said, and he truly was sorry. "I wish I could stay, but I must go back to Tulagi. My wife will soon have a new baby and I must be with her and my other two children," he explained.

The chief was not ready to give up just yet. "Then, please, Masta, leave somebody here to teach us more," he begged.

Norman shook his head. After pleading with God to open these islands for the gospel, he had to leave them to be with his family. And he needed the whole crew to operate the boat.

Just then the young cook boy who had just come from a heathen village, stepped up. Only 16 years old, Imbi said, "Masta, *me* stop."

Norman looked at him. It wasn't possible. "No, Imbi, you can't stop [stay]," he said. "You know very little of the gospel stories in the Bible. You cannot teach the people."

But the boy disagreed. "Masta, me savee long picture roll. Me stop!" [I understand the stories, let me stay.]

And so that evening the boat sailed from Koilotumaria, leaving 16-year-old Imbi to teach the people the love of Jesus through songs and stories, using the Bible picture roll. The next day, October 24, 1932, a second son, Ervin, joined the Ferris family.

"No mistaking that you're the father of this boy," the doctor told Norman. "Not with so much dark, curly hair." Baby Ervin grew into a calm, contented, happy little boy who brought much joy to the family. Little did they know that someday God would enable him to continue his father's work in the Solomon Islands.

Unknown to Imbi, back in the village of Tenabui the devil again appeared to his priest. As Nghata began his morning incantations a voice commanded, "Nghata, you failed to kill the White man. But he left a boy to teach the people. Take your sword and kill him, and do not fail this time!"

Immediately Nghata returned to his devil house and prepared himself to go to Koilotumaria once more. But suddenly he fell desperately ill, so much so that he thought he would die. While he lay in a state of delirium, an angel appeared to him. Startled, the sick man gazed at this white-robed being. Then he heard a strong command: "Nghata, do not touch the one whom Jesus has appointed."

As he relived the strange visit from the angel of light his mind began to clear. Why would the mighty Warrior send an angel messenger to him? What plan did this great God have for him? Almost immediately a great change came over this wicked devil priest. In his sickness he pleaded, "Strong Power, help me to forsake my evil ways. I long to learn of this mighty Warrior, Jesus."

Lying there Nghata wondered, *Will He ever teach me how to do good and not kill?*

When he recovered from his sickness Nghata decided to talk to the boy, Imbi. This proud, cruel man, now humbled, begged the boy, "Please come to my village and teach my people. I will care for you. I do not want to follow the fallen angel, Satan, who ordered me to kill you."

Imbi gladly shared the love of Jesus with Nghata's village, telling them all the Bible stories he knew. He taught Nghata and his people to sing praises to God, too. Sometime later Norman again traveled along the coast. He stopped to visit at the village of Koilotumaria. What a difference!

Imbi hurried to his Masta. In Pijin English he told Norman how he asked for God's Spirit to help him share his faith in all the villages in that area. And now, instead of devil chants, the songs of Jesus' love rang through the jungle morning and evening.

Best of all, Norman had the privilege of baptizing Imbi and the man he brought to Jesus, Nghata, the first convert in this region. Like the apostle Paul on the Damascus road, God transformed Nghata into a mighty worker for God. No longer did he join Satan in his hate campaign against Jesus. By gentle and patient ministry, angels and the Holy Spirit moved upon Nghata's heart.

He joined with angels to share God's love and compassion for these fallen and unholy villagers.

Many months later Imbi married a local girl who had learned to love Jesus. Their son, Imbi, Junior, when grown, continued on in the gospel ministry.

This once lost man, Nghata, became a missionary himself. As day followed day, he learned to love Jesus more. He learned that when Jesus takes him to heaven he, Nghata, will tell the angels a story they cannot know. No longer a devil priest, he will tell the unfallen worlds how Jesus made him into God's own son.

Transformed by the Holy Spirit, God used Nghata to raise up two churches in the Tambuti area. Today, along that coast of Guadalcanal, men and women and children in 16 thriving churches with more than 2,000 members sing those same beloved songs. Better yet, God blessed the next generation in opening several schools and a thriving boarding school where young workers continue to be trained to serve Nghata's God.

THE BROKEN STICK

Near the end of the nineteenth century, a passing missionary anchored his ship off the coast of Rennell Island. He made no attempt to go ashore, but led his crew in singing gospel hymns. Fascinated, a few of the Rennell boys paddled their canoes to the ship and with an invitation, climbed aboard to listen to the singing. Planted in the heart of one boy, Tapongi, the son of the paramount chief of the village, was a great desire to learn to sing those hymns and know that God. Sitting on the deck of that little ship, he experienced a peace and joy he never forgot.

As he grew up, he often thought of this God who loves—the One about whom those sailors sang. Would he ever understand about this "Jesus loves me" who seemed so different from the devil gods his people worshiped?

Years later, after young Tapongi became chief of the village, a crafty devil priest came to the people with vicious lies. First, he claimed to be Jesus. Then he lied, declaring a bright angel appeared to him with the horrific message, "You must kill all unmarried men plus any man with a scar on his body." The simple village men believed these lies from the devil priest. Since the village had a shortage of girls, unmarried men began to murder married men to get their wives.

Young Chief Tapongi, now the paramount chief, hated these evil ideas and longed for a way to end this senseless murder. He realized he needed help to govern his people with wisdom. If only he could find a missionary who knew this God of love. Maybe the missionary could contact this God power who could stop the hatred, fighting, and killing among his tribes.

So Chief Tapongi made a plan. Secretly, he took a reliable boy name Panio to the beach. "Take your canoe and go to nearby islands and find a missionary who can teach my people to sing the White man's hymns," he instructed the boy. "Find one who will tell my people about a God who has the power of love. Here is a stick. I will break it in half. I'm going to keep one half of the stick and you must give the missionary the other half. Then when he comes and we match our sticks I will know he is the right man."

For four days Panio paddled, following the clouds that he thought led him to an island. But he had no knowledge of the ocean currents that swept him farther and farther out to sea. Without food or water he became desperate. However, the God he did not know kept watch over the boy in the canoe who had been sent to find a power stronger than the devil.

All this happened in 1932. Shortly after Panio left, a sailing ship in search of water made contact with Rennell Island. This remote island lies 150 miles southwest of Tulagi, then the capital city of the Solomon Islands. The trader who was also captain of the ship met the paramount chief, Tapongi, whose tribe lived in the great Tagano Lake district on Rennell Island. After obtaining water, the trader continued to his destination, Tulagi. Many miles from land he saw the boy in the lone canoe and took him aboard. Through translation, the trader learned of the broken stick and Chief Tapongi's request for help. "I know of only one man that I can recommend," the trader told the boy. "If you can find him you can trust him to help your chief and your people."

Again God was in control. He arranged that Norman Ferris needed to make a trip to Tulagi at the same time the trader arrived. The man recognized him.

"I have a boy named Panio on board from Rennell Island," the trader told Norman with some excitement. "His chief sent him to find a missionary who would come and teach his tribe gospel songs and a better way to live. When I saw you, I told the boy that you are the White missionary who would come and establish a mission in his village. Come to my ship and meet him."

Gladly Norman joined the trader. With help in translating, the trader told the boy that he had found the right missionary who would come and fulfill his chief's desire. As soon as Panio understood, he darted down into the hold of the ship, returning with an odd-shaped stick that seemed to be broken in half. With great feeling Panio begged that missionary Ferris visit his people soon. He handed him the broken stick with these words: "Present this stick to Chief Tapongi. He will know that Panio sent you."

Some months later Norman received permission from the government to visit Rennell. Though no missionary could remain on the island, the government granted permission for natives to leave their island and receive schooling. However, they must return to teach their own people.

As soon as they possibly could, Norman, Panio, Pastor L. S. Borgas, and the ship's crew made their first visit to Rennell Island. With many prayers that they would receive a favorable reception from the people, they landed at a small sandy beach that had a devil house erected near the shore.

Soon a tall man of kingly appearance stepped forward. He saw Norman and he saw Panio. "I am Chief Tapongi," he announced to Ferris. "I am also a devil priest. Are you that missionary?"

The chief produced half of a stick. Immediately Norman put his hand into the bag he carried and brought out the broken stick the boy had given him. Tapongi examined it carefully, nodded his head, and smiled. "Come to the lake and my village. My people have been waiting and longing for a teacher to come."

Norman thrilled at meeting a friendly group of Polynesian men, six feet or more tall and well built. Many strong men, bodyguards of the chief, carried their bundles of long spears and clubs. Both men and women had many tattoos on their bodies.

Norman discovered that these people had a vague understanding of "Big Master on top" (God in Heaven). All welcomed their visitors with smiles. Chief Tapongi explained, "For a long time I have desired to know how to sing those hymns that I heard as a young boy. Now I am growing old. I want my sons to have the fulfillment of my hopes."

The chief took them on a well-worn but slippery path. They could see the inland lake, 10 miles long and three wide. At last they came to the village on the edge of the lake. The chief invited them into his house, and they crawled in through the low door on their hands and knees and sat on the floor. Moa, one of the chief's sons who spoke good Pijin, acted as the main spokesman. This young man pleaded passionately for a teacher. "Five months you come back. You no forget us. Come back quick time."

Still the government would not allow any teachers, Black or White, to remain on the island more than one day. But the chief did allow six boys from Rennell Island to go with Norman Ferris to learn to read, to sing, and to learn of this God of love. With intense feeling Chief Tapongi allowed his eldest son and Moa to join the other boys, trusting Norman to take them to Batuna School far away in the New Georgia Islands and to keep them safe.

Broken Stick

Moa quickly gained a knowledge of the English and Marovo languages. With help he translated 30 hymns into the Rennell language, which were then printed. He could read and sing them when he returned to Rennell. Best of all, Moa gave his heart to Jesus. As Norman saw Moa's enthusiastic love for Jesus, he prayed that this intelligent young man would become a missionary to his own people. When Norman brought those boys back to Rennell five months later, he prayed with them that they would stay true to the Creator God. He had to leave the island before sundown but when he left, some more boys came with him to go to school. Eventually 16 of the boys on Rennell Island went to the missionary school.

However, when Moa returned from Batuna to the heathen environment, he soon lost his contact with God. He quit praying and reading the little book of God he had once loved. As his relationship with Jesus began dying he again was attracted by devil worship. He went wild, and joined with other wicked young men. He followed the devil priests and for a time he used his leadership talents to fight and kill.

But God listened to the prayer of faith of a young missionary family in Guadalcanal. God loves to combine His supernatural power with His children's persistent prayers. He chooses to grant that which He would not bestow did they not ask. One day as Moa and his wife worked in their garden they heard a voice calling, "Moa! Moa!" They looked everywhere but saw no one, so they went back to work.

Again Moa heard his name, and again he answered, but looking around saw no one. But suddenly he was overwhelmed by a powerful longing, an intense desire, to serve Jesus. Right there in the garden Moa and his wife fell on their knees and determined to serve one Master and follow the Sabbath mission. That night in a dream, Moa saw Jesus who spoke to him. "Though no missionaries can come to these islands, I am sending you to make your people strong in the love of God," Jesus told him. "When they have chosen to serve Me, then go to Bellona and tell the people there the story of Jesus' love for them. Teach them to worship the Creator God."

When Moa woke up he awakened his wife and told her of the dream. She immediately promised to join with him, to stand nobly by her husband and the true God.

The next day Moa began mission work in his own village starting with his brother, Tekehu. "My brother, God's Holy Spirit showed me from His Bible book that Christians must separate from the old devil worshipers. We must start a new village some distance away. We must build homes along the lakeside, too far for our children to have easy access to any heathen village. Will you go with me?"

Moa's new village, called Hutunga, became a model of neatness and order. In the center of a clean compound they built a church. New converts joined them to carve the floor out of limestone. With joy for their newfound God they worked hard to smooth it off to give the effect of cement finish. They carved seats out of large, insect-resistant logs. Together they shaped the timbers that held the roof out of the same beautiful wood which gave the appearance of cedar. Thatch proved to be the best roofing material available.

Around the square stood the tidy homes of the people. Since money did not exist on Rennell Island, Moa and his helpers planned an interesting feature for their village, a tithe house, the place they kept their tithes and offerings. Down by the shore of the lake, Moa built his home. He painted a sign on a box which read, "The Head Office. S.D.A. Mission, Hutunga, Rennell Island."

Moa and his wife became a living demonstration of what the Spirit can do and will do in preparing people for the coming of Jesus. They showed their love for God, trusting Him to help them keep His commandments. One by one they brought others into their village and taught them the ways of Jesus. Moa and his wife became a spectacle on their island to angels and to men, for their lives glorified and honored God by their good works. Then Moa ventured out to nearby villages. When they learned of Jesus he went farther afield to share Jesus' love for humankind.

Unfortunately, government rules restricting visits from outsiders continued, as many diseases had been spread to the villagers, introduced by passing ships. Several more years passed without Norman having any contact with Rennell, but he and others continued to pray that God would open a way to bring more gospel truth to these people. A few letters began to creep through with news of the missionary work Moa and others did for the love of God. Eventually, four boys from Rennell traveled across the open seas in a canoe to call for help. When government officials went to Rennell to investigate, Moa made a strong protest that no one should seek to control the spiritual welfare of his people. These officials found that Moa and his helpers had consistently shared their faith and love for Jesus, for a large number of people on both islands claimed to belong to the Seventh-day Adventist Mission.

One day Norman received a letter from Moa pleading for him to come and visit them. When the comissioner read the letter, he said, "We can't keep these people isolated any longer. We must do something to help them." Thus God opened the way for Norman go to Rennell.

When they anchored off Tahuggo beach, the first person to meet them was Panio. He was there in his canoe, now a young man. When he saw Norman, he shouted his welcome.

"Oh, Master, heart belong me full too much. Me can't talk. Me fellow pray long Jesus, sun he come up, sun he go down. Me thank Him Big Master on top. He hear pray belong me fellow."

Yes, much praise and joy went heavenward from Rennell! Their missionaries had come!

Later an angel again spoke to Moa. "Now you must go to Bellona," he instructed Moa. "Destroy all the wood and stone devil gods. Teach the people about the Jesus God who is coming soon. Show them how to live so they can go to heaven with Him. When you have destroyed the devil worship, build churches for a new kind of worship with gospel songs and Bible stories."

Moa gathered a few other young men who had gone to the mission school at Batuna and who continued to follow Jesus. They set out in their canoes to be missionaries on the island of Bellona, some 17 miles to the northwest.

Determined not to release his captives, immediately Satan determined to make life difficult for these boys. Tension increased. When Moa went through part of the island smashing all the wooden and stone devil gods, 300 men met and decided that they must kill Moa. Probably Tiekika (Thunder and Lightning) joined these 300 furious warriors as they rushed toward the missionary, demanding vengeance for what he had done.

Surrounded by shouting, angry faces, clubs, and spears, the young missionary knew he faced death. He remembered the courage he'd seen when Norman Ferris stood fearlessly before these very warriors and their leader, Tiekika, and Moa sent up an urgent plea to God.

At that, the power of the Holy Spirit came upon him. He bravely stepped forward and spoke with courage. "The power of Jesus Christ is stronger than that of Satan," he said in a strong voice. "I challenge the devil to get out of Bellona."

Instantly, the warriors calmed down. They laid their weapons on the ground. Without resistance they watched Moa step up to a large cave claimed to be the devil's abode. Suddenly a very large white crab came to the mouth of the cave. Out of the mouth of the crab came these words: "Moa, you have half of the island, but give me the other half."

"NO!" Moa responded. "In the name of Jesus Christ whom I worship, and whom I serve, you devil god get out of the island altogether."

Moa remembered the story of the pigs in the Bible as he and the warriors watched that huge white crab amble over to the edge of the cliff, jump into the sea, and disappear. Then right before them, Moa smashed one of their sacred devil stones.

Again, wild with anger, they grabbed their long spears and danced around him, shouting threats to kill him. Suddenly, as if silenced by an unknown power, the men sat down and their spears fell to the ground. Moa declared, "Me no afraid. Me do Him work for Jesus. Me die. Me ready."

Before the quieted mob, Moa stood up. "You saw an unseen power drive the devil's white crab to the cliff," he began. "The power of Jesus, the Creator God, made him go. All your life you have followed the ugly power of that terrible evil angel, the devil. He hates you and makes you do bad things. You are not happy. Now the good angels will come to Bellona. You each have a strong, powerful good angel. He will speak to your mind and tell you good things. You will have peace and joy. The good angels serve the God who heals your sicknesses, who makes your gardens grow, and who protects you when you go fishing in the rough seas. When the devil comes to hurt you, if you call, 'Help me, God of heaven,' He comes immediately and the devil must flee."

Moa continued, "Jesus told me in a dream to come and teach you how to live this happy life. If you let Him, He will make you ready to live with the Eternal God. Now, will you decide to depend on His power to guide you? The God of heaven will never leave you nor forsake you. But He will never force you like the devil did. You must choose Him each day. You can know the love of Jesus. Soon He will come and take you to live in His wonderful home called heaven. Do you want to give your lives to this wonderful God?"

Moa stopped to let them think. Finally they began to ask questions. Slowly they grasped the incomparable love of Jesus as shown in His death and resurrection that Moa had told them about. As they listened, they began to see the ugliness of devil worship contrasted with the beauty of worshiping a God of love. This new way of life seemed good to them. As Moa discerned their change of attitude, he began to lay plans for building churches in the various villages.

After seven weeks of witnessing the Rennell boys reported that all the people on Bellona had left their heathen practices. Yes, even Tiekika (Thunder and Lightning) gave his proud heart to God. True, he had lapses where he defied the leadership of others, but his thunderous demands erupted less and less. Slowly he allowed God to humble him, and he became a leader for God in his village.

No doubt, during this conversion time, the angels looked upon these fallen men—once children of wrath—with astonishment. Through the power of Jesus they began developing characters after His divine life. From being pawns in the devil's hands they now desired to become sons and daughters of God. One day, when Jesus comes, they will act an important part in the occupations and pleasures of heaven. Even now, imagine the joy in heaven and in the unfallen worlds as the inhabitants listen to these dear people sing songs of praise as they worship in their eight new native churches. Day by day, as they cooperate with heavenly Beings, God will finish what He began in the lives of these transformed Bellonese Christians.

CHAPTER 1: ABOVE
The beach on Bellona where Thunder
and Lightning (the name an explorer gave
Chief Tiekika after a frightening encounter)
leaped off the rock in foreground to challenge Pastor Ferris on his arrival at their
sacred bay.

CHAPTER 1: ABOVE
The rock from which Thunder and
Lightning and his warriors jumped
onto the sand.

CHAPTER 1: RIGHT
Kata Rangoso
climbing hill to inland
Lake Rennell.

CHAPTER 2: ABOVE
Norman, age 14, with his dad on
Norfolk Island.

CHAPTER 2: ABOVE
Norman (top left) at age 16 with his brothers,
sisters, and mother on Norfolk Island.

CHAPTER 2: ABOVE
Norman and his two brothers, Walter and David. All three were missionaries in
Solomon Islands.

CHAPTER 2: LEFT
Norman as a student
at Avondale College.

CHAPTER 2: RIGHT
Group at Avondale
College in 1922.
Norman and Ruby
are pictured in center,
in front of the tree.

CHAPTER 2: ABOVE
Norman and Ruby with their wedding party.

CHAPTER 2: RIGHT
Pastor and Mrs. Ferris leave for Solomon Islands with other missionaries on March 16, 1927. From left to right: Mr. and Mrs. J. D. Anderson and children, Brother G. Peacock (superintendent of Solomon Island Mission) and wife, Pastor A. G. Stewart (Union Conference vice-president for the mission field), Mr. and Mrs. Norman Ferris.

CHAPTER 2: LEFT
Norman met his daughter, Norma, for the first time in 1930, in Lord Howe Island, where his parents lived.

CHAPTER 2: BELOW
Family picture taken at Norfolk Island when Norman was reunited with
Ruby and the two children.

CHAPTER 3: LEFT
Norma with her daddy, Norman.

CHAPTER 3: RIGHT
Kata Rangaso as a young man
when he rescued baby Norma.

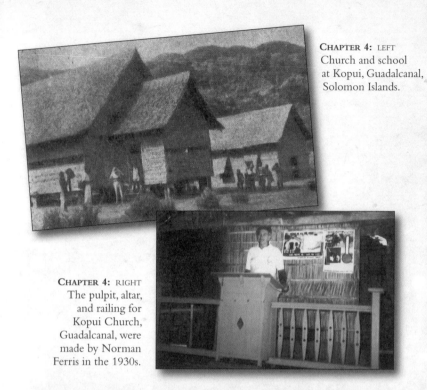

CHAPTER 4: LEFT
Church and school
at Kopui, Guadalcanal,
Solomon Islands.

CHAPTER 4: RIGHT
The pulpit, altar,
and railing for
Kopui Church,
Guadalcanal, were
made by Norman
Ferris in the 1930s.

CHAPTER 6: ABOVE
Six boys from Rennell Island with Norman Ferris and Pastor Borgas.
One boy is Moa who later challenged the devil at Bellona.

Pastor Ferris preaching on Bellona Island.

Pastor Saika pointing to the spot where Pastor Ferris
met Tapong with the broken stick on Rennell Island.

CHAPTER 7: LEFT
Photo taken when Pastor Ferris went with Kata Rangoso to the SDA General Conference in San Francisco, and became ill with typhoid fever.

CHAPTER 8: RIGHT
Pastor Ferris and Kata Rangoso.

CHAPTER 11: ABOVE
Pastor Ferris at Torokina, Bougainville with Okira, Hoke, and Tati, three outstanding workers that helped during World War II.

CHAPTER 11: BELOW
The *Portal* after it was restored.

CHAPTER 11: LEFT
The *Melanesia*, the flagship of the mission fleet in the Solomon Islands.

CHAPTER 11: RIGHT
The *Melanesia* crew with Pastor Ferris.

CHAPTER 12: LEFT
Wilfred Bili

CHAPTER 13: RIGHT
Sir Ronald Garvey, governor
of Fiji, asked Pastor Ferris to
go to Pitcairn Island to govern
the island. Later, Queen Elizabeth II awarded Ferris the
Most Excellent Order of the
British Empire (M.B.E.) for
his years of mission and medical service. Sir Garvey and
Ferris at the award ceremony.

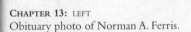

CHAPTER 13: LEFT
Obituary photo of Norman A. Ferris.

"Not now, but in the coming years,
It may be in the Better Land,
We'll read the meaning of our tears,
And then, sometime, we'll understand."

-MAXWELL N. CORNELIUS

CHAPTER 14: ABOVE
Nghata, former devil high priest, meeting Mrs. Ferris after 55 years.

CHAPTER 14: RIGHT
)th Anniversary celebration
at Kollatamonia village
on Guadalcanal.

Pictured:
orma, mother Ruby, Ervin,
and Marilyn.

Chapter 16: LEFT
Matthew makes a call for commitment and several people from Savo Island responded.

Chapter 16: RIGHT
The island where new Savo Christians went to get away from persecution and to attend baptismal classes with John Sota.

Chapter 16: ABOVE
Distribution of clothes to new converts on an island near Savo after the islanders lost their clothes.

Chapter 16: left
The rascal, his wife, and 15-year-old daughter on Savo Island.

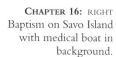

Chapter 16: right
Baptism on Savo Island with medical boat in background.

Chapter 16: above
Welcome following the baptism at Savo Island.

CHAPTER 16: LEFT
Ervin Ferris with
John Sota, his wife
and baby, and another
convert at Savo Island.

CHAPTER 16: ABOVE
Savo Church built
by Fly and Build Team.

CHAPTER 16: LEFT
Ervin Ferris at
Savo Church.

CHAPTER 16: LEFT
Children that the naked little boy from the mountains saw through the trees.

CHAPTER 18: ABOVE
Three living Ferris children who helped in Fly and Build team.

Left to Right:
Norma, Ervin, Marilyn.

CHAPTER 18: RIGHT
Typical house in Kopui Village.

CHAPTER 18: ABOVE
Kopui SDA high school, Guadalcanal. Administration and classrooms.

CHAPTER 18: ABOVE
Girl's dormitory
Kopui SDA high
school, completed
in 2006.

CHAPTER 18: RIGHT
Kopui Boy's dormitory SDA high
school, Guadalcanal, completed
in 2007.

DISAPPOINTMENTS AND VICTORIES

How did God help Norman Ferris manage to supervise so many projects? Where did he find time to give counsel and leadership to the growing leaders in the various islands, villages, and churches without neglecting his family?

Whether his family traveled with him on the mission boat or lived in their home at the Kopiu Mission Station, the children always saw Norman show kindness, love, and affection for them and their mother. Each morning and evening he called the family together for worship. As he lovingly told Bible stories about Jesus and His Father, the little ones joined their daddy in the same precious relationship. Following Daddy's example, they longed to be like Jesus.

Both Norman and Ruby served as doctor and nurse to their family. Though not medically trained, they understood most of the tropical ailments and how to treat frequent attacks of malaria.

One Friday night Norma suffered greatly with a toothache. On Sabbath morning her dad took her on his lap. "I'm so sorry, my dear Norma, that you hurt so badly," he sympathized. "I don't have any local anesthetic to deaden your pain. But I must be your dentist and pull out that tooth that ached all night long." He explained that the tooth was far back in her mouth so she wouldn't miss it. Hugging her close, he added, "I feel sad that I have to hurt you so much, but it won't last for long."

Norma saw tears in her father's eyes as he kissed her. When she grew older she forgot the pain, but she never forgot how her father carried her around in his arms after pulling the tooth. In memory, she could still feel the warmth of his great love.

That same love and trust endeared Captain Ferris to his boat crew and other native workers and teachers. As explained earlier, one man, Kata Rangoso, became a close and beloved friend. Then one day in 1936 a special message came from Australia to both of them.

The message read, "Kata Rangoso and Pastor Norman Ferris have been chosen as delegates to the 1936 General Conference to be held in San Francisco, California. Pastor Ferris will be his interpreter. Rangoso will probably be the first Solomon Islander to step ashore in North America."

The leaders at the mission headquarters suggested that while Norman was away Ruby and the children should return to headquarters in Batuna. Ruby disagreed. She explained to Norman, "I'd rather stay right here in our home. Living with another family with three lively young children doesn't appeal to me. Besides if any emergency happens, we have a reliable boat and a caring crew."

While Norman was away, the secretary-treasurer, Pastor Barrett and his wife, Hilda, occasionally came to check on Ruby and the children. This particular time they arrived on a Friday. With the house cleaned and cooking done, the house girl had picked a lovely bouquet of orchids and brought them inside. Everything was spotless. Ruby welcomed her friends and they all looked forward to a happy weekend.

Then without warning the house began to rock. The hibiscus flowers in the study crashed on the polished floor. All the bottled medicines in the bathroom fell and broke, their contents running in a stream. The milk in a pot on the stove slopped around. Another Guadalcanal earthquake left their house a terrible mess!

Outside, the ground seemed to come up to the hill in waves. Time and again, the Ferris family ran out of their house for safety as the tremors continued to shake everything. After each quake a tidal wave followed, wiping away everything near the water's edge.

Shortly after the quake Ruby received word from Norman, sent when their ship docked for a day in Fiji. He told of a happy get-together of workers, but mentioned that typhoid fever ran rampant in Suva, Fiji. Many of the workers who'd planned to attend the General Conference in California could not go due to illness. Norman's next message—this one from California—stated that Rangoso thrilled the listeners with his stories of the many miracles among the former headhunters. He spoke in the Marovo language with Norman interpreting for him. Norman ended the letter saying that he felt another attack of malaria coming on..

Church headquarters in Sydney, Australia, soon learned that doctors had put Norman in a San Francisco hospital and were giving him copious doses of quinine. However his symptoms grew worse. When he started to hemorrhage, tests proved he didn't have malaria but typhoid fever. Thinking it best not to worry Ruby, they decided to keep the situation from her.

However, they had no way of knowing that Norman had written to Ruby from the hospital. His condition became so critical that he'd asked a nurse to write a "goodbye" letter for him to Ruby and the children.

This letter arrived by freighter the morning that Ruby and the children landed in Tulagi to get their monthly supplies. Indescribable anguish overwhelmed her. Frantic, Ruby sent a cable to Sydney. Word came back: "Norman much improved. Do not worry." Frequent messages came to and fro until finally she received word that he would return on the next available ship.

Meanwhile in San Fransisco, Rangoso visited his dear friend in the hospital. "Pastor Ferris, we planned to travel all over the United States visiting many camp meetings on a lecture tour. Now doctors tell me you will be in the hospital for at least six weeks. Can you give me any counsel? What shall I do?"

Pastor Ferris held out his thin hand. Rangoso grasped it. Slowly Norman spoke. "I am so disappointed to miss this great privilege. I do not know of anyone who speaks the Marovo language. Would you be willing to take this tour without an interpreter? You must not disappoint the many people who look forward to meeting you and hearing what God is doing for your people."

"You mean I must speak in English before large audiences?" Rangoso looked frightened.

"I realize that the English you speak is mostly 'textbook English'. However you do read the language well. I feel certain that God will help you express yourself with clarity. He will enable you to adapt to every situation. Trust Him, Rangoso. God has power to do great things through you."

At last Rangoso told Ferris, "I know I can never do this without His divine help. But I remember you quoted the promise, 'His biddings are enablings'. Please pray constantly that God will bless my feeble efforts."

Assured of his friend's powerful prayers, Rangoso agreed to travel without his help while Pastor Ferris recovered in California. Later Rangoso admitted to his dear friend, "America became a great school for me. God used your illness to further the work in the Solomon Islands. Because I must speak English,

God used this to improve my knowledge of the language. I know this will make me a much better translator of the Bible into my language."

Several doctors examined Norman when he finally arrived in Sydney then came to him with their conclusion. "Pastor Ferris, we concur it is very unwise for you to return to the tropics just yet, and we advise you to remain in Sydney for six months to recuperate. We suggest your wife and children return to Sydney to be with you."

What joy to be a family again! Progress seemed slow while they stayed in a hostel provided for such emergencies, but finally the doctors released him. Now that he could work again the mission committee had new plans for him. "We want you to spend much time visiting and helping the various mission stations around Guadalcanal. Unfortunately, you will be gone from your family again. Since your wife is expecting your fourth child, we suggest she and the children remain in Sydney until after the birth of the baby."

On July 6, 1937, baby Marilyn Francis joined the Ferris family. Very much interested in missions and how God blessed this mission family, Ruby's doctor asked, "Mrs. Ferris, what is your greatest need in your mission station? Is there anything we can do to make your life more comfortable?"

"Doctor," Ruby answered, "I'm taking this new baby back to an unscreened house where malaria mosquitoes abound."

"Thank you for telling me of your need. We will have your home measured and order the best screens be made to fit all doors and windows." The doctor smiled as Ruby's face lit up with joy.

She was thrilled. "I shall ever be thankful for this wonderful gift," she assured him. "I have lived in the tropics for 14 years and have never known such comfort."

When the doctor released Ruby and the new baby to travel back to the Solomon Islands, they met Norman at Tulagi. The entire family traveled together to Batuna to attend the mission committee meetings. While traveling back to Guadalcanal in the mission ship, they encountered engine trouble.

After taking everything apart, Norman discovered that someone had stuffed crushed dry coconut leaves into the fuel tank at some point when the crew had left the boat unattended. Before morning this problem was solved.

Tired from working most of the night, Norman and the exhausted crew took a nap while just one man stayed at the wheel. But 4-year-old Ervin had slept all night in the cabin and he woke up early. He got up and came out to the deck, making little sailing boats out of coconut shells with sails made from leaves. As his mother watched him, he kept saying, "Look, look. My boats sail." Just then he put out his hand to swing around the guy rope, not knowing it had been removed. Instantly little Ervin slipped overboard and into the sea.

"Ervin's overboard!" Ruby shrieked. "Ervin's overboard!"

But the men who had been up all night slept soundly. Frantically praying, she started to jump into the water to save him when she heard in the distance, "Dad! Oh Dad!" With great thankfulness, she remembered that Ervin's Solomon Island nurse had taught him to dog-paddle as soon as he could walk. This saved his life. After what seemed ages to the concerned mother, the skipper turned the boat around. They threw a life buoy to little Ervin and a crew member dived in and bought him back to the boat.

Yes, the Ferris family kept the angels busy. When Satan brought sickness and troubles, God continually heard their requests to send His power. Jesus, their constant Companion, always kept His promise, "I will never leave you nor forsake you."

8

WORLD WAR II
AND THE SOLOMONS

War clouds loomed on the horizon. The Japanese, in their southward thrust, headed for the Solomon Islands and warships plied the Pacific waters. The government set up Coast Guard stations around the islands. As the situation became more serious, the security guards advised the Ferris family, "Send your older children to Australia for safety. In case of emergency, your burdens would be less without all four of your children. Do you have someone who could care for them?"

"Yes," Norman answered. "My wife's mother has always been willing to help us."

"Then we'll help you make arrangement that they leave on the next ship for Australia. Please contact their grandparents immediately." This they did.

As time passed, the Japanese continued conquering in their thrust southward. Next the Solomon Island government ordered, "All women and children must take the next available steamer to Sydney, Australia." Crowds waited at the wharf to board. Again Norman and Ruby had to part for a time, their hearts breaking. Norman held Ruby and baby Marilyn close, wondering when he would see his dear family again.

A cyclone was threatening when the full ship left Tulagi. The ship tossed and rolled in the heavy waves and many passengers became seasick. Feeling the need of fresh air, Ruby made a quick trip to the deck. At that moment a searchlight picked up their ship and played all over it. She ran back inside announcing, "Searchlight! Searchlight!"

Even as the ship wallowed in high seas, the order came: "Muster to the dining room. Bring your survival kits." The motley throng came carrying babies in their arms and buckets to catch their vomit. All seemed paralyzed with fright, fearing a raider was bearing down on them in this dreadful sea. After what seemed hours the captain came to them with the news, "You may return to your cabins but use no lights. An Australian squadron going north to help the Singapore government spotted us."

With great rejoicing, they arrived safely in Sydney a few days later. Ruby thanked God that once again she could be with her older children.

Japan's string of victories astonished even the Japanese. They had advanced successfully in their southern thrust in the South Pacific. After the Japanese bombed Pearl Harbor, America joined the Allies. With lightning speed the Japanese advanced toward Malaysia and Singapore. Rabaul fell to them on January 25, 1942, precipitating orders for all Australian men to leave the Solomons.

When the missionaries left, the SDA mission committee chose Kata Rangoso to be responsible for the interests of the Seventh-day Adventist Church. Norman, forced to leave their comfortable Kopiu home, left behind all their furniture and belongings. He wondered if the Japanese would confiscate all of it.

In his haste to flee from Guadalcanal, Norman had mistakenly picked up a box of charts he'd made of the safe routes through the dangerous reefs and atolls around Guadalcanal. The Navy had heard of them, and urgently needed this information. Upon his arrival in Australia, the customs officials took the charts.

The church appointed Norman youth director of the South Australia Conference and sent him and his family to Adelaide to live.

In the meantime General Douglas McArthur, who had an office in Sydney, heard of these important charts and immediately sent an officer, Captain Hines, who knew Norman Ferris, to Adelaide with orders to: "Locate him, intercept him, and bring him to my office as soon as possible."

Since the Ferris family had moved into a fully furnished house out of town it was not convenient for Ruby to do shopping, so one morning she handed Norman a written list of a few things she needed. "During your lunch break," she said, "would you please go to the store and get these items?"

About noon Captain Hines began searching for Norman Ferris. As he walked down the street, he paused before the entrance of a store and Norman walked out.

"Well, Ferris, I do not believe in your God, but I am sure He arranged for this meeting. Please make arrangements with your employing body, say goodbye to your family, and come with me to Sydney to talk to General McArthur."

During his boat travels in the Solomons, Norman had come across an uncharted reef and had put a pencil mark around that area. The charts confiscated by the customs officers had already been delivered into General McArthur's hands. McArthur informed Norman that this penciled area might be the same place where the Americans planned to engage the Japanese.

Details of conversations between Norman Ferris and General McArthur have been kept secret, but the fact is that Ferris needed to share his knowledge and experience to help the general with plans for the U.S. Marines' landing on Guadalcanal, which happened on August 7, 1942. Some weeks later General McArthur released him and Norman returned to Adelaide.

The six-month battle for Guadalcanal was one of the most vicious campaigns of World War II. Fearing attack, the Australian government gave orders to civilians as to the procedure should an invasion occur on their continent. From the Solomons sad tidings of severe stress for the nationals came rumbling, though minus any detail, during those horrible war years. Finally after the two atomic bombs were dropped on Hiroshima and Nagasaki, the Japanese surrendered unconditionally on August 14, 1945.

Because of the problems facing the national workers in the Solomons and his love for these dear people, Norman requested that he return to give help and assurance to those who had suffered during the Japanese invasion. He resigned his position in Adelaide, found a small house near Avondale College in Cooranbong for his family, and joined a troop ship going through to Bougainville. From there he worked his way to the Marovo lagoon where he met with his old friend, Kata Rangoso.

"Please, may I tell you of God's protecting care during the war," Rangoso asked with a smile. "So much happened since you left."

"Please do," said Norman. "I'm anxious to learn everything that happened while I was gone, and eager to see our dear people again. If only we had a boat so we could visit all the faithful workers who struggled and endured so much these three years."

GOD'S SOLDIERS IN ACTION

Rangoso grasped Norman's hand. "Do you realize that it was only about 20 years ago when I was a devil-worshiping heathen boy, that I first met a White missionary? The responsibility laid on me when all of the missionaries left would have overwhelmed me if I had not known that His grace is sufficient. With the Japanese so close, I knew I must act quickly so I called all the national leaders to come to Batuna. "We must make plans to work together and depend wholly on the Lord," I told them.

"I'm sure God gave you much guidance and improved your natural talent for organization," Norman interrupted.

"God did help me, again and again," Rangoso continued. "When Pana, my cousin, and Jimaru, my younger brother, arrived with many others, we met at the church and prayed earnestly for wisdom and guidance. So before the Japanese landed on our islands we made plans to construct buildings deep in the jungle, well hidden, and accessible only to those of us who know the jungle well. There we could hide all movable equipment and goods. Second, we'd hide the remaining small boats upriver. The boys would camouflage them with greenery, palm fronds, and branches."

"Next, we trained first-aid parties to care for the wounded and dying. We formed classes to teach everyone how to set broken bones and sew up wounds with a thorn for a needle and raffia thread for sutures. Scouting parties must be organized to spot and search for airmen whose planes had gone down. We made canoes ready to rescue sailors who survived when ships sunk. Only through Jesus' guidance could we succeed to bring healing and love when all around we faced hate and death. After earnest prayer we returned to our islands determined to be ambassadors for God."

"The Japanese landed soon after Pana and Jimaru arrived at their homes," Rangoso went on. "With their families they fled, walking upstream through river beds to obliterate their footsteps. They built temporary shelters in secluded spots. Meanwhile the Japanese stripped the well-equipped hospital that Pana had operated, taking the timbers and galvanized iron to line the foxholes and trenches they dug around the beach. The Japanese destroyed our church and our gardens, and burned our homes. And yet when our people faced starvation they came upon gardens in the jungle and felt certain that Jesus had sent angels to plant them months before.

"One day Jimaru and his children found a burned plane, a water bottle and other equipment, but no trace of the pilot. Then they looked up and saw a man suspended in the branches 40 feet high, hanging by the lines of his parachute. Together they piled a large mound of ferns and leaves and Jimaru called, 'You come down long tree.' Finally the fearful airman decided to release himself from the harness. He had a broken arm and severe cuts on his face.

"Using a crude stretcher, they carried him for hours to the cave where they hid. His deep gashes did not permit him to eat even crushed bananas so the men and boys hunted for birds' eggs. They mixed them into coconut milk and made a nourishing drink he could swallow. Then Jimaru told him, 'If you want to live, I'll boil water in this coconut shell, sterilize this thorn, and make thread from this vine. Sadly, I have nothing with which to put you to sleep. First, I must talk to God asking him to give you strength to endure the pain.'

"'Go ahead,'" the airman consented. 'I want to live.' Though he cried out in agony, he fell asleep when Jimaru finished.

"Several days later, after Pana set the airman's arm, he endured the rough trip of going through the enemy's forward lines to an American hospital near the air base."

Norman put his hand on Rangoso's shoulder. "I praise God for your leadership in this brave work. Now please tell me what happened here at Marovo Lagoon?"

"A runner arrived with the news that a huge Japanese ship would soon arrive so a British major commanded his men to flee using the mission boats. The motors of two boats started immediately, but the temperamental engine of the *Portal* refused to start. We heard his command. 'Pour gasoline over everything and set it on fire so the Japanese won't get it.' Immediately a sheet of flames roared to the masthead. The major never saw us Christian islanders drop to our knees and plead with God to save our beloved mission launch.

"Suddenly the praying men saw what seemed like an invisible blanket smother the fire. God's boat would not burn!"

"Praise His name!" Norman exclaimed. "Where did you hide the *Portal*?"

"At high tide we pushed it into the mouth of a little creek, completely camouflaging it with jungle materials."

Norman clasped his hands together in joy. "Did the Japanese ever find the *Portal*? Where is the ship now? How did the British treat you as leader?"

"One question at a time, please," replied Rangoso with a smile.

Then he grew serious. "I'm sorry to tell you that a British Coast Guard officer who hated religion accused me of not cooperating when I refused to order my people to work on Sabbath and to bear arms. He arrested me as a traitor and put me in prison. Again and again he cruelly beat me. And then, in his insane rage, he commanded a soldier to shoot me, but the gun would not fire. In frustration, he beat me with the handle of his gun until I fainted, lying raw and bleeding. When I came to, soldiers marched both my friend Londi and me back to prison at gunpoint. The officer told us he'd force us to wait out the war in prison.

"During this time, the Christians in the Marovo area beat out drum messages calling all believers to pray for us," Rangoso continued. "They longed for their imprisoned leaders whom they loved. Then shortly before midnight on May 29, 1943, a tall man with a bunch of keys walked to the prison gate, unlocked the padlock, opened the gate, and called, 'Kata Rangoso, come here! Londi, come here!'

"Awakened from sleep, we went to the gate. Taking each of us by the arm, the man drew us outside, shut and locked the gate, and led us down the path to the beach. We heard what sounded like a bird call. In a moment a canoe approached the shore. In the boat we met our friends. We both turned to thank the man who released us, but he was not there. In the bright moonlight we scanned the path for more than 100 yards, but could see no one."

Norman quoted a favorite promise, "It is a part of God's plan to grant us, in answer to the prayer of faith, that which He would not bestow did we not thus ask" (Ellen G. White, *The Great Controversy*, p. 525).

"Before my prison wounds had healed, I organized watchmen every five miles along the island coasts to search for Allied planes and warships. They brought reports to me regularly. Immediately I sent men to locate and care for the survivors.

"Our workers always fed the survivors from their meager food supply. Once the Japanese torpedoed a warship carrying 187 Australian and New

Zealand soldiers. I sent out many canoes to rescue those still swimming in the ocean. We fed and cared for them until a radio operator located another warship to take them aboard."

Ferris could not help interrupting. "I can hear King Jesus saying to all of you, 'Come, you blessed of my Father, inherit the kingdom prepared for you . . . for I was hungry and you gave Me food; I was thirsty and you gave Me drink; I was a stranger and you took Me in'" (Matt. 25:34, 35).

"But some of our faithful teachers paid a heavy price for their dedication in rescuing Allied military personnel," Rangoso said sadly. "Do you remember Deni Mark?"

Norman nodded.

"He kept on teaching in our training school, though surrounded by the Japanese. For many months he brought food to an Australian Major whom he had secretly hid in the jungle. Then the major asked him to make a map of just where the Japanese were entrenched

"Some time later Deni returned with the drawing. He accurately located every gun, hut, and building occupied by the Japanese in that area. In one corner he drew a house with the words, 'House belong me. No bomb please.'

"The Japanese continually harassed this brave teacher. Life became very difficult for his wife Esther and their six small children. One Sabbath a soldier demanded, 'Send your school children to help us today.'

"'No, sir,' Deni Mark said. 'Our God asks us to worship on the seventh day. We will help you any other day.' The soldier flogged him severely time and time again. This severe punishment proved too much for this brave man, who became very sick. Just before he died on September 15, 1944, he called his wife and the school children to him. 'I promised God and Kata Rangoso to serve,' he told them. 'Please, you carry on for me.'

"Just after his death Esther and the six little children had to flee to the jungle, enduring terrible dangers and much privation. Finally with much prayer they reached safety."

Norman reached out and grasped Rangoso's hand. "Thank you so much for letting God use you to lead these brave Christian warriors. All of you fulfilled God's promise in Ephesians 2:6, 'And raised us up together, and made us sit together in the heavenly places in Christ Jesus.'"

10

Brave Men and Teens

Rangoso, still eager to share stories of the loyalty and bravery of God's younger children, said to Norman, "You need to know the quality of the Solomon Island youth. May I tell you about Elakae, who claims he has a bigger story of God's rescue than the disciple Peter who was rescued from Jerusalem's prison?"

Norman nodded eagerly. "Please do."

"Elakae said, 'Masta, Peter e' only got few soldiers watch 'im, me 500 or a thousand plenty.' He had just turned 17 when the Japanese took him captive and forced him to guide several regiments of soldiers through the difficult mountain areas which had many sulfur pots and other dangers they wished to avoid.

"The sulfur fumes from the volcanic blowholes smelled more pungent than usual as they made their way along the narrow trail. Only the trained eyes of a native who lived in the jungle could see such a trail for at times it seemed to be entirely swallowed up by the steamy jungle. Often the boy felt the prod of a bayonet to remind him of his task as a prisoner to lead these men over the hazardous mountain track.

"At night they threw him some food and then bound him hand and foot, placing him in the midst of the soldiers to get what rest he could. Both physically and mentally exhausted, Elakae had come to the point that he felt he could stand the torture no longer when he remembered a promise he'd learned—'He shall call upon me, and I will answer him; I will be with him in trouble; I will deliver him, and honor him' (Ps. 91:15).

"'Dear God,' he prayed, 'I'm just a Black boy, but I have given You my heart. Is that promise for Black boys, too? If so, please deliver me.' Exhausted and comforted he fell asleep. Sometime in the night he was awakened by a crash of thunder. Lightning flashed and crackled, and rain fell in sheets like a flood. The air smelled strongly of sulfur.

"The Japanese soldiers were terrified. Seized with panic and overwhelmed with fear, they screamed and fought with one another. Fighting with their bayonets and rifles, madness ran riot. They forgot all about their prisoner. The boy feared he would be trampled to death when he suddenly realized his wrists were free. A moment later a flash of lightning revealed that bonds no longer tied his feet together.

"Realizing God had answered his prayer, Elakae crawled on hands and knees through the struggling soldiers until he gained the shelter of the friendly jungle. Like a shadow in the night, he made his way over those mountain trails until he reached the cave to which his own people had fled to escape the invaders. Though he arrived past midnight, none slept. These faithful Christians were praying earnestly for their boy. Suddenly he stepped into their midst saying, 'God saved me. Here I am.'

"No wonder he said, 'Masta, 'im' 'e story belong Peter 'im 'e only lik lik [little] story. Story belong me 'im 'e big fella [bigger] story.'"

Norman laughed. "He's correct. Great story. I'm proud of boys like him. Do you have at least one more youth story?"

"Oh, yes, I do. This took place when the Japanese pursued about 25 American soldiers. The Americans had hired a number of native boys as carriers of important materials, and the boys, knowing the area, led the way. The heavily armed American commandos brought up the rear.

"About 5:00 o'clock that Friday afternoon the captain said, 'We are only about three hours short of comparative safety.' But just before dusk the column of carriers halted. The captain rushed to its head, wondering what was wrong. He discovered that the carriers had dropped their bundles and were busily prepared to make camp.

"'No, no!' he shouted. 'Carry on. In less than three hours you will be home.'

"The boys shook their heads. 'No, we stop. We make camp.'

"'You must go on!' he shouted even louder. 'The enemy will catch up with us. All of us will be killed. You, too.'

"The head boy of the carrier line went to him, saluted smartly, and said, 'You look 'im sun, you look 'im 'e go down. God's day 'e come up. We stop.'

"By this time the rest of the commando group had reached the carrier boys. They added their orders to carry on. But the firm and only answer they received was, 'Sun 'e go down, God's day 'e come up. We stop.'

"So stop they did. Not only did they rest all night, but all the next day until the sun set. Then those boys, with a smile, picked up their packs and resumed their journey. Upon arrival the captain learned that if they had continued on Friday night, they would have walked straight into an ambush and all would have been killed.

"With deep gratitude the captain declared, 'This is more than chance. God honored the faithfulness of those boys who honored His commandments.' To my knowledge this is the only time a company of American soldiers halted, forced to rest whether they wanted to or not. Why? Because Solomon Islander boys remembered God's Sabbath."

Ferris spoke slowly. "Imagine the joy those boys will feel when Jesus Himself places crowns on their heads and invites them into heaven saying, 'Well done, good and faithful servant; you have been faithful over a few things, I will make you ruler over many things. Enter into the joy of your lord'" (Matt. 25:23).

11

GOD'S FIRE EXTINGUISHER

Between the time when the Japanese left and the British could return, many non-Christian Solomon Islanders pillaged the stores and homes of the government, trading, and mission personnel. As soon as possible, a British officer came to punish the offenders. He commanded that the people in the villages where the stealing occurred stand some distance from their homes and watch while the police set fire and burned all their homes and belongings.

When they came to the Seventh-day Adventist village of Tuki, teacher Joseph whispered to the chief and people standing in line, "They'll burn our church, the schoolhouse, and everything in our homes including our Bibles and hymnbooks. Let's ask God to protect us from this bad time."

The police scattered dry coconut leaves on the floor of the chief's house, then poured kerosene on the leaves and set fire to them. The faithful villagers prayed aloud as they watched the flames leap from the windows and the door. But as soon as the leaves burned themselves out, the fire stopped. Puzzled, the police brought more palm fronds. They poured much more kerosene on them and lit the fire again. The people kept praying and praising God. Again when the fire burned up all the coconut fronds, it went out.

"Shall we try a third time?" the police asked the officer.

"No. Some strange power seems to control this village. Let's go on."

The next morning the officer called Rangoso to come on board his boat. "You'll have no trouble with looting now," he said. We burned all the villages but one. I tried repeatedly to burn their chief's house, but it wouldn't burn."

"Which village was that?" Rangoso asked.

"Tuki," he said.

Rangoso smiled. "My younger brother, Joseph, teaches there. In this Adventist village no one looted the White man's goods. God protected His innocent children."

The officer shook his head. "I'm sorry. I wish you had told me before. Your people stay true to their God and their faith in Him. If I had known, I would not have tried to burn their village."

———

During the latter months of the war, soon after the Allies landed on New Georgia, another burning plane plunged into the lagoon. The American pilot parachuted into a clearing where he saw a village hidden by greenery. Landing near the huts, he felt pain in his arm. Slowly he forced himself out of his parachute and crept carefully through the jungle, making as little noise as possible, fearing that his head would become another trophy for the headhunters he'd heard so much about.

All the huts seemed empty. In the center of the village he noticed a large structure with a slab floor raised on posts. Cautiously he walked toward the building, climbed the rough wooden steps and peeked in the door. Aloud he said, "That's strange. Wooden benches in even rows, up front a crude railing, pictures of Jesus on the walls. Must be a church. Guess I'm among Christians, not headhunters."

The airman relaxed on one of the benches. Then he noticed a jar filled with dead flowers sitting on what looked like a pulpit. As he sat there thinking, he became more aware of the throbbing pain in his injured arm. But then a strange feeling of peace overwhelmed the pain. He recalled the days when he once loved the Bible stories he heard in church. In his mind he again heard the prayers of his mother.

At that moment he heard a bird screech from the jungle. Rising slowly he walked to the door and peered out. Two Black men stepped into the clearing. He called and waved to them. The younger one spoke in halting English, "You American or Japanese?"

"I'm an American pilot," he said as he walked toward them and extended his hand. All three men smiled. The older native explained. "I'm chief of this Seventh-day Adventist village. I help our leader, Kata Rangoso, find pilots who fall down in the jungle."

The younger man climbed a coconut tree and slashed off several green coconuts. With one whack of his big knife, he sliced the top off one and of-fered it to the pilot for a drink.

"Delicious!" he said after gulping it down. He drank a second one more slowly.

"My people now hide in the hills," the chief explained. "A Japanese scouting party stays near our village. I will go to my people and they will come with food and the medicine bag." Soon some villagers arrived with fruits and vegetables, and a young man from their group cared for the airman's wounds. At sunset the people all gathered in the church. "You come, too," they beck-oned. Never had this American heard such singing. To him he thought, *They sound like a choir of angels.*

Several days later they heard the sound of an airplane. "That's from Amer-ica," the nationals shouted as they ran down the hill to the beach. Waving pieces of cloth, they attracted the plane. As soon as the American arrived at the beach, he signaled with a mirror. The plane circled, buzzed twice, and dis-appeared.

Several hours later an amphibian plane landed on the lagoon and some of the villagers took the airman out in a canoe. The plane's nose hatch opened and a friendly face looked out.

"Hi, Tex!" the young man said with a grin. "So you're hobnobbing with fuzzy-wuzzy headhunters. I see your head is still fastened to your neck."

The pilot grabbed the hand extended from the hatch. "Listen, man, these guys live like super Christians and I believe their Master Pilot, Jesus, guided me to this village," he said. "You should hear them sing in their church every morn-ing and evening. I've never been treated so well. All because they obey their God and a guy named Kata Rangoso. He and God must be runnin' this show."

Then the airman turned to his new village friends. "Thank you for these marvelous stories."

———

"Now tell me about the *Portal*," Norman said. "Word came to us from the British that they burned it to keep it from falling into Japanese hands. Could this be true?"

Norman saw some of the listening men run to get their canoes. "Where are they going?" he asked.

"To get the *Portal*," Rangoso smiled. "That boat belonged to God. Planes often flew over, but it stayed hidden."

To Pastor Ferris the launch looked like a wreck. He wondered if it were still seaworthy. For three years it had rested in the still waters of a mangrove creek. Surely insects and rot had rendered the hull useless by now.

The islanders quickly cleaned up the boat. Not one sign of a worm or a borer could be found. "Surely God took care of His boat," Norman exclaimed. "She'll look like new when we replace the awnings and rigging."

But the pastor let out a cry of despair when he reached the engine room.

"Oh, no! All that's left is the cylinder, flywheel, crankshaft, and crankcase. Everything small enough to be carried away is gone! There's no hope now for visiting the surrounding islands."

He turned to look at Rangoso and the others. Surprised he saw only smiles, not the dismay he felt.

"The engine is all right," Rangoso assured him. "We have everything." He turned toward the men. "Go get all the parts," he said.

Again the nationals scattered, arriving back with bits and pieces of the engine which they had safely preserved throughout the war. Their drums beat the message that it was time to bring back parts for the *Portal* and for days villagers arrived with more and more of the intricate pieces needed to restore their precious craft.

For almost three weeks the people happily worked together restoring the boat. Being a diesel mechanic, Pastor Ferris had no trouble getting everything in place. While they put the engine together, others worked on replacing the missing rigging, masts, and awnings.

Finally they came to that tense moment. Would she start? A former crew man filled the tank with fuel and lit the blow torches. Another wound the rope two times around the flywheel. The engine boy gave a shout and pulled. An even greater shout went up from everyone as the once temperamental engine sprang to life. Once again the *Portal* would take God's messengers to tell the story of love to those who live in hate and darkness.

Only one sign of the effort to destroy the *Portal* remains. Like the scars that will remain on the hands of Jesus throughout eternity is a patch of heavily charred timber close beside the cabin door that shouts in Pidgin English, "Portal 'im 'e boat belong God. 'Im 'e no burn!"

In the later part of 1945 Pastor Ferris and another missionary spent several months traveling thousands of miles in the *Portal*. They visited many mission stations, praying with and encouraging the teachers and pastors. The U.S. Army gave them as much diesel as the mission fleet needed, fuel aplenty. The American forces also supplied iron and other materials to rebuild their schools that had been damaged or destroyed during the war. And they reimbursed the mission for the property confiscated or lost during the war years.

Seeing the need to train the young people to be leaders, Norman secured wonderful land not far from Henderson Air Base in Guadalcanal. (This land is about 10 kilometers inland from the small but growing town of Honiara, now the capital city of the Solomon Islands. Other missionaries established Betikama Adventist High School/College there in 1947.)

From 1945 to 1946 God helped Pastor Ferris reorganize the mission work that had been so rudely interrupted by the war. Very soon the islanders left their hiding places, glad to be back in the villages and spreading the gospel story.

12

WILFRED BILI'S STORY

Tragedy struck soon after Norman returned to Australia to be with his family. Raymond, their eldest son, died from an accident at his work. Ruby and Norman were devastated with grief. At the Division year-end meetings church leaders asked Norman to be dean of men at Avondale College. Gladly they accepted, for Ray's grave was only half a mile away. Also the other three children could live on the Avondale campus as they attended school. The Ferris couple became like mother and father to the youth who referred to them as Pa and Ma.

In November 1949 the first youth congress outside of North America convened at Avondale College. Delegates, appointed from all over the Pacific Islands, attended the conference, including three boys from the Solomons. Pastor Ferris met these three boys when they arrived by ship. Thugea Bili, one of the three, showed outstanding character traits. Ruby Ferris wanted to get better acquainted with this energetic boy so invited him to a meal at their home. In gratitude he asked, "May I help you wash the dishes and do other chores around the Ferris home? I can even milk your cow."

The Ferrises learned to love this fine young man from Guadalcanal. However, Ruby had a difficult time pronouncing his native name, Thugea, which means, in the language of the mountain people, "Ask about him."

"Would you mind if I changed your name?" she asked after they'd become well acquainted.

"Not at all," he replied. So she began pronouncing many names, beginning with biblical ones. Finally she said, "Wilfred." He stopped her. "That's the name I want." From then on he became Wilfred Bili. Flashing his shy smile he asked, "May I tell you my life story so you'll understand why my parents gave me that strange name?"

Wilfred's father, a very wicked devil priest and witch doctor, went by the name Bili Beruka. He lived in a village high in the mountains of Guadalcanal. Before Wilfred's birth, he accepted from the devil an extremely cruel and wicked spell called *vele*. This horrible power killed all the people in many villages in the mountains of Guadalcanal. Briefly, this is the devilish practice he used to kill anyone he wanted dead.

If any man who owned this horrible spell heard someone at a distance shouting or whistling, he would put this invisible spell on the little finger of his left hand. If someone looked to see where the sound came from, the witch doctor would swing his arm and hand around. All people within the arc of his swing would turn red, regardless of their skin color. Then each one would fall unconscious.

When the devil priest casting the spell would come to each of his unconscious victims he would wake them up. The victim would have no knowledge of what happened so was not able to tell family or friends what he'd gone through. In addition the victims were unable to speak until about 9:30 in the evening. Often the spell would cause them to leap up and swing from the beam of their house. When they dropped to the floor they would be dead.

When the colonial government came into power in the Solomon Islands, the government determined to stop this senseless killing. In their first attempt they arrested 11 men suspected of using this horrible power. Taking them to Tulagi, then the capital of the Solomons, the men were tried in court. Wilfred's father was one of them. Ten of these devil priests were hanged. Only Bili Beruka was placed in jail to await execution, one of his wrists and one ankle chained to the locked cell door. Police guarded him 24 hours a day. He could find no way to escape.

Word came that Beruka would be hanged at 9:30 the next morning. That night he slept until about 2:30 a.m. and awoke with the thought that this was the last morning of his life. With difficulty he managed to stand up in the cell. Suddenly he felt the miracle power of the devil and saw his chains fall to the floor. Now free, he reached through the bars of the door, put his hand over the head of the police guard, and cast a spell that would keep the man unconscious about two hours. Why did God permit the devil to work those miracles? Could it be that God, who knows the future, saw wonderful possibilities, not only in this wicked man but in the son not yet born to him? Dressed like a jungle bushman, Beruka took off. When the policeman awoke he saw the empty cell with the chain and lock on the floor. He shouted the alarm but none of the searchers could find him.

Bili fled to his mountain home but left again, telling his wife and relatives he would try to hide. But first he grabbed his bag, a small axe, a razor to shave his beard, a box of matches, and his devil worship trinkets. He found a little island in the center of a swamp where he hid for three months. He had no food, but in his bag he had another devil miracle object he called an *otho*. When he felt hungry he placed it against his stomach and instantly he felt as if he'd enjoyed a good meal. Then he put it back into his bag until he needed it again, believing the devil sustained him. Again, why did God allow this devil miracle, this strange power, to keep him alive for three months without eating? Could it be God's tremendous love to save vile sinners? Or could it be to show the onlooking universe God's compassion for those who believe the devil's lies?

After three months on the island Bili found another place to hide in the jungle. Three months later he found yet another hiding place. This he did for eight years. During that time, thanks to his devil power, he had a constant supply of matches. Hidden among the trees he'd see someone stop to rest and light up his pipe. That person could not see him, but he always left his box of matches which Bili Beruka took. This experience was repeated many times and he never ran out of matches.

Finally the government heard that this escapee still lived and sent word to his village: "The law reads that a fugitive will be declared free after five years and may go home." During those many years interested people often stopped by to ask his wife, "Have you heard from him? Is he alive?" When Beruka returned he built a house by the side of a river and formed a new village. Two years later a baby boy arrived. His mother called the baby, "Ask about him," for the word *thugea* means "ask about the baby's father."

In the early 1940s a missionary from the next village came to see Wilfred's father every week. For five years he continued to come, asking for permission to start a church and school in their village. But the devil, his father's best friend, kept preventing it. At last the missionary seemed to give up, for he did not come again. But after some time he returned. This time Beruka agreed to let him start a school and to let a group meet at the school each Sabbath to worship. He himself refused to come, but many in his village came, heard God's message, and believed, and kept God's Sabbath.

Then one night God gave Wilfred's father a dream. Two angels dressed in shining white came to his house. They put a little bench beside the door, sat down on it, and said to him, "This is the way of life. What are you waiting for? Join them." And then they departed.

The next morning, Sabbath, Wilfred saw his father sitting by his mother in the back seat of the church. His father had chosen to listen to those two angels. After a lifetime of devil worship, he resisted the devil. And just as the Bible promises, the devil fled from him. Soon after this Beruka asked for baptism. Not long after his baptism he became very sick. Realizing the seriousness of his illness, he called for the missionary. "I want to thank you for what you brought to my village," he told the missionary. "I know that I am going to die. I have nothing to give you in appreciation. But I do have a fine boy. Please take him. If he is good, use him. If he is naughty, send him back."

When Wilfred heard that his father made him a gift to God, his life goals began to change. "Why did God choose me?" he wondered. "I'm the son of a man who spent his life with Satan in his hate campaign against God? Why did God send angels to my father, a man so wicked, so unworthy? Will God teach me how to experience and reveal His love to others? I cannot read, so I do not know how to study His Word." He determined to go to school and learn how to serve this great God.

The missionary told him of the school at Kopiu, located on the flat land by the ocean. So Wilfred left his mountain village to attend this school. In two years he completed primary school at Kopiu, then heard that a secondary school had opened near Honiara. So he enrolled in the first class of the new Adventist high school at Betikama. His teachers recognized that this young man had a vision for service and chose him as one of the three youth who would represent the Solomon Islands at the youth congress—where, of course, he met the Ferrises. After spending two months in Australia, inspired by "Ma and Pa" Ferris, Wilfred returned to the Solomons. It was 1950.

To his surprise, the local leaders asked him to work in the mission office. He almost turned it down. "I have no training for this job," he told them. Instantly came the thought, *God knows I have very little schooling. So every opportunity must be God asking me to accept and learn as if I'm in a classroom.* This became his philosophy in life.

For the next 45 years Wilfred Bili held many responsible positions in a variety of the Pacific Islands mission offices and also in Australia. He learned bookkeeping from the treasurer, who showed him how to handle and record all the financial matters. God blessed his mind and he learned to do business transactions perfectly. He kept the books in 11 different mission offices, then became treasurer, always doing his work for God. God gave him discernment to be the assistant president at Bougainville.

Later mission leaders asked him to go to Sonoma Adventist College in Papua, New Guinea. They informed him, "We have appointed you as the one who will prepare the young ministers at the college. To do this you will need to teach these eight subjects."

Wilfred looked at the list and objected. "I have never taken classes in ministerial training. I know nothing about these subjects. Where are the materials?"

They handed him a stack of books. He almost said, "No, I can't handle this. I've never even studied these subjects." But God impressed him with the thought, *Ignorance is no excuse. Accept this new challenge as a school in which to learn. Trust Me. I gave you this opportunity to learn.* For six years he taught pastors and students throughout the islands. Like Solomon, Wilfred pleaded with God for wisdom and God granted his request by "giving him a wise and understanding heart." Throughout his years of service, Wilfred purchased 3,000 books. He studied them, giving himself assignments, searching for answers.

Since the people in almost every island in the Pacific speak a different language, God gave him another gift for which he did not ask, the gift of tongues. Wilfred expressed amazement at his ability to quickly learn languages. In just the Solomon Islands alone, he learned 11 languages. His usual procedure followed this pattern—with God's help. For about two weeks Wilfred would listen carefully to people speaking the language he wanted to learn. By that time God enabled him to understand and speak it. Then he continued to enlarge his vocabulary and reading ability. He now is fluent in 16 languages. He had no instruction in learning to speak English. Though it was difficult, God enabled him to speak English without an accent. He constantly reads and studies to improve this ability, thanking God for this spiritual gift of tongues.

When this boy, who came from the vilest of environments, chose to accept God's grace and love, God endowed him with many talents. Now retired, Wilfred continues to serve his people and his church. At the same time he improves his mind by deep Bible study and the pursuit of the books in his library. Most of all he longs to improve his character by looking to Jesus who is changing him into the same image from glory to glory.

BROKEN STICK

Because Christ took on human nature, He can present His children to His heavenly Father. Then God will confer upon them an honor exceeding that conferred upon angels. "This is the marvel of the heavenly universe, the mystery into which angels desire to look. This is love that melts the sinner's heart" (Ellen G. White, *Sons and Daughters of God*, p. 22).

Yes, even Wilfred Bili and his wicked father.

13

PITCAIRN CHALLENGES

While in the Solomon Islands, Norman and Ruby Ferris became acquainted with a young British cadet named Ron Garvey who served in the colonial service in the Solomon Islands. With their usual fondness for befriending young people, they frequently visited with Ron and he learned to admire the tact, kindness, and service of love he saw in the Ferrises. He especially admired Norman's methods of missionary outreach with the local people. In addition, Ron's respect for the lifestyle of Seventh-day Adventists deepened with his friendship with Pastor Kata Rangoso.

By 1951 Ron had been advanced to Governor of Fiji, which meant he had control of Pitcairn Island. Unfortunately, much unrest had developed among the people on Pitcairn. Sir Ronald Garvey decided that he knew only one person who could settle the problems between the factions. He needed a kind, tactful leader to organize the little community of about 150 people into the smallest colony of the British Empire. He contacted Pastor and Mrs. Ferris. "Please accept the position of the governor's representative to act on my behalf on Pitcairn," he told them.

So they set sail for this isolated island, only two miles square, which lies about 5,000 miles east of Australia. After eight days of calm weather they arrived about midnight on December 5, 1952, in a heavy rainstorm. All their cargo was drenched and damaged by the water, but the problems they faced on this small island were even worse. Later Pastor Ferris explained that "Only the workings of the Holy Spirit in Christian fellowship and renewal brought about transformation toward a friendlier atmosphere on the island. Our first week of prayer, a happy time, solved old problems. From that time, the sounds of prayer and singing could be heard in many homes."

God used Pastor Ferris' many talents to teach the men and older boys how to repair engines, build new boats, and keep the women's sewing machines in running order. They trained the youth in first aid, and taught and practiced simple remedies to care for the sick.

Some years before, the islanders had purchased a launch to help them tow the longboats that carried fruit and curios to the passenger ships that stopped nearby. Unfortunately the engine never worked. So Pastor Ferris helped them tear apart the engine so they could repair it. However, the flywheel would not budge. They tried everything including rust removers and wedges, but the wheel remained stuck fast to the shaft. After three days of trying, the engineering trainees went off fishing and several discouraged men suggested, "We'd be better off to tip it all into the sea."

Pastor Ferris felt dejected, especially as the men had begun to build a new boat to house the restored engine. Left to himself, he looked at the stubborn flywheel, wondering what to do. He decided to pray again.

"Dear Lord, You know I've come to the end of my ability. Your wisdom and strength far surpass mine. You have helped me again and again. Please take over if this experience will bring honor and faith in our heavenly Father's name. Thank you."

Before he could say "Amen" Norman heard a noise and a bang. The flywheel lay in the bottom of the boat. Again Jesus demonstrated the power of prayer and faith. Norman called the men to him. With joy in their hearts they soon had the engine overhauled. Within days the new launch went into service, hauling the heavy longboats.

When their year was up, the people of Pitcairn requested that the Ferrises stay another year, and the government granted their wish. This gave Norman additional time to help with more problems. The existing church—made from discarded lumber and worked over by white ants and termites—was a disaster. Again Norman held a prayer meeting asking God for financial help. Soon generous gifts came from tourist ship passengers and the mission. Then some friends sent California redwood for pews, chairs, and the rostrum. They received corrugated roofing iron and other materials *and* free shipping. The island men worked voluntarily with Pastor Ferris to construct the new church, and it was dedicated just three months after work began.

While Pastor Ferris attended mission meetings in Fiji, Sir Ronald Garvey requested he come to receive a special award at a dinner in Suva. The award honored his service to Christianity and the empire, including his service outside of mission work in caring for the sick, plus his engineering projects on Pitcairn. The queen acknowledged the 17 years he had spent in mission service in the Solomon Islands both before and after the war, awarding him the Most Excellent Order of the British Empire. The queen made Norman Ferris a member of the British Empire with many privileges. For the rest of his life, behind his name he carried the honor of M.B.E. (Most Excellent Order of the British Empire) after his name.

In his acceptance speech Norman Ferris stated, "I accept this honor not for any personal gratification but for the honor that it brought to the cause of Christ in the South Pacific Islands. This award from Her Majesty, Queen Elizabeth II, vindicates that she approves of the presence of the Seventh-day Adventist church on Pitcairn Island." And for four happy years Pastor and Mrs. Norman Ferris gave loving service to those who lived on the lonely island of Pitcairn.

The last two years of his life Pastor Ferris devoted in loving service to the aborigines of the Mona Mona Mission in North Queensland, Australia. Then on Monday afternoon, July 7, 1958, Norman and Ruby drove into the city of Townsville. The driver of an oncoming car, approaching at great speed, could not negotiate the bend in the road and hit the Ferrises. Both cars were completely demolished, and Pastor Ferris was fatally injured. Ruby suffered from triple fractures of her right leg, a broken arm, painful lacerations on her head, and extensive bruises.

But most of all she suffered from the loss of her dear, patient, loving husband. At first she felt like nobody without him. But as she recovered she found that God truly does care. He enabled her to live to serve others for more than 40 more years. Constantly, she thanked God that soon she and Norman with those who believed in Christ will all sit together with Him upon His throne. Ruby died at 103 years with the promise, "He will silently plan for thee in love."

Instead of thinking of the circumstances of Norman's sudden and tragic death, almost too painful to contemplate, Ruby could only say with the inspired poet:

"Not now, but in the coming years,
It may be in the better land,
We'll read the meaning of our tears,
And there, sometime, we'll understand."
(*Church Hymnal*, 1941, No. 495, Maxwell N. Cornelius)

GOD CONTROLS WIND, WAVES, AND LOGS

Did the influence of Norman Ferris' life stop after 54 years of service? Not at all. Were all the sacrifices, problems, and tropical diseases treated by a missionary mother with four children worth the loneliness and frustrations? Did their years of dedication make any lasting difference in the lives of those who worshiped the devil?

The answer came loud and clear in 1989, when a large fiftieth anniversary celebration convened at Koilotumaria village on Guadalcanal. They invited Ruby Ferris and her three living children, Norma, Ervin, and Marilyn to join them for this celebration of God's power. At that time the district had seven churches with a membership of 1,800. (By 2006 about 5,000 loyal members from 16 Seventh-day Adventist villages in the area gathered weekly for worship together on God's holy Sabbath.)

Ruby's heart thrilled with praise to God for what He has done since the day Nghata, the devil priest, tried to kill her husband and later 16 year-old Imbi. Great joy filled her heart as she clasped Nghata's hand, a living miracle of God's power to change a murderer into a man who leads others to love Jesus.

Where sin abounds, God's grace much more abounds. These people who know by experience what it feels like to be saved by the mercies of God, gathered around the memorial plaque they had placed on a pedestal. Ruby stepped forward and with tears running down her cheeks read aloud: "Seventh-day Adventist Church, Tasamite, Guadalcanal, 58th Anniversary, 1932-1988. On October 20, 1932, Pastor Norman Ferris with Imbi and others at the invitation of Kaomane Mau landed on this spot and commenced the work of the Seventh-day Adventist Church in this district in loving service to God and man."

Turning to the people crowded around the area she said in a clear voice, "I never felt that the years my husband and I spent in the Solomons had accomplished very much for the gospel. Today I've spent many happy hours renewing acquaintances with dear friends and national workers with whom we worked in the 1930s. No longer will I wonder if our service for God had lasting results. I have seen with my eyes your young people attending the beautiful school beside the river, the very river where my husband baptized Nghata. I've heard you singing praises to God. I've seen your faces expressing joy and hope. I praise God for victory over the devil's power."

———

Has the power of prayer and dedicated service continued in the lives of young volunteers from Australia and the Solomon Islands? Consider what God does even now through dedicated youth. Many gladly join the Fly and Build program started by Norman's son, Ervin, a retired missionary pastor. See for yourself what God does when young people give their time, energy, and money to build schools, churches, and clinics and to conduct evangelistic meetings. To them this is a joy, not sacrifice.

While constructing a school on the large island of Choiseul, the volunteers took the day of rest to enjoy the Sabbath by crossing the bay to a small isthmus island. Here they met with the Nuatambu Adventist community. As the volunteers looked around the old, run-down village church they discovered the foundations for a new church higher up on a hill. Unfortunately, the jungle encroached the foundation from every side. A young volunteer, Ervin's son, Rayden, asked the village elder, "How long ago did you lay this foundation?" The team crowded around to hear the answer.

"Sixteen years ago we decided we needed a permanent church here, but we could not progress beyond this foundation for lack of timber. No roads provide access to the big trees we own that grow 16 miles up the mountain from here. Even when we cut the logs into smaller pieces, several men struggle through the jungle and down steep slopes with the heavy load. When we reach the ocean, we must put the logs onto canoes and paddle each one across the isthmus to the portable sawmill near the church site. We kept trying, but our members found the tough journey long, slow, difficult, and almost impossible!" His voice dropped in discouragement. "Lately we've been asking God to help us find an easier way to get the timber to this building site before the Fly and Build team arrives."

"Humanly speaking your prayer sounds impossible, but that doesn't take God into consideration," Ervin Ferris, the team leader, told them. "As you know, we've chosen to make the building of your church our next Fly and Build project, but our first requirement is that the local people provide the foundation and all the timber cut into boards. We provide the portable sawmill and other materials to complete the building. And as you understand, we must have the timber ready and cut before the team members arrive to build."

All around him the church members shook their heads. Some of them had been to the mountains to cut down those huge trees. Some had spent hours sawing them into logs that they then struggled to bring down the mountain. It seemed impossible. They did not have enough men or muscle power to accomplish this huge task.

Smiling, Pastor Ervin pointed heavenward. "Remember, God loves to do the impossible," he reminded them. Little did he know that God had already begun to answer those sincere prayers.

A manufacturing company from Taiwan purchased the timber rights from a village adjacent to Nuatambu. They brought in heavy equipment such as tractors and road graders, and cut through the trees to make roads so that logs could be dragged down out of the mountains to the seaside. When they had enough logs, a large ship, anchored about one and a half miles off shore, waited to take the logs on board and then to Taiwan. But to get the logs from the shore to the parent freighter, they must be loaded onto a rented barge that could navigate in the shallow waters of the isthmus. Then the barge, pulled by a tug, would take the logs to the freighter's crane which would lift them up to the ship.

Meanwhile the church members continued to think and struggle with the impossibility of getting down the mountains enough timber to build the church. And if they could manage that feat, it was all but impossible to load the timber on canoes and then paddle across the sea to the building site. It became obvious that they could never accomplish all this before the deadline when the Fly and Build volunteers would arrive.

During this interim the Taiwanese freighter was anchored in the waters beyond the bay, waiting to load the logs from the barge onto the ship. The tug slowly pulled the barge through the narrow isthmus and out into the bay to be off-loaded onto the freighter. As the tug left the shelter of the bay into the open sea, a extremely strong wind whipped the sea into high waves. As the tug neared the ship the sailors faced great difficulty trying to manipulate the barge close enough to the ship for the logs to be loaded. Suddenly a violent gust of wind slammed the barge against the side of the freighter. The barge hit with such force that a small protrusion on the side of the ship punched a hole in the barge about a foot below the water line. Immediately water poured in and the barge began to sink.

To prevent losing the barge, the sailors worked feverishly with the freighter's crane to unload 30 very large logs into the ocean, knowing it would be hopeless to try and retrieve them in the rough water. The Taiwanese just let them go. As they floated on the sea, it seemed that all 30 logs were being guided by the One who controls the wind and waves. Each log in close proximity to the others washed up on the beach about 200 meters from the foundation of the church that was to be built. Did God hear the prayers of His people from Nuatambu? He surely did!

When the church members discovered those huge logs, they knelt on the shore in gratitude. "Great and mighty God, who controls the land and the sea, thank you that for 16 years You were planning for us in love. All that while you listened to our prayers for help. You gave us strength and hope to continue to do our feeble part. Thank you for sending that powerful wind. In a short time You created circumstances which gave us the logs. How gracious of You to guide them to exactly the right place."

Immediately the men brought the Lucas portable sawmill to the site from the opposite side of the isthmus and began work to cut the logs into boards. Before the Fly and Build team arrived, the church members carried the boards up the hill to the church site. Now they were ready for the builders. God's gift of timber lay all cut and neatly stacked.

The entire community witnessed what their mighty God did at just the right time. He loves to do more than we can ask or think. The church, housing 400 members, completed in June 1997, sits on a hill overlooking the bay, a monument to God's power when people pray. But while they prayed they continued to wait on the Lord, trusting His goodness and doing what they could, however little, to the glory of God.

15

FLY AND BUILD BIRDS

Many miles from Choiseul lies the large island of Guadalcanal. In the inland mountains live people who have worshiped the devil all their lives. No one has shared with them the love of Jesus. They do not yet know they are the children of the God of heaven. In these heathen villages the people invite their pigs into their houses, letting them sleep with their children. From this source of infection and the filthy lifestyle conditions many villagers contract a skin disease called black ringworm which covers the body from head to foot.

In the village of Aola a heathen mother and her two daughters, all three suffering from this ringworm, heard that young people had hiked in from the coast to a nearby village. Their purpose, to show the villagers how to live healthfully.

After the girls listened to more village gossip they rushed home excited to share the news. "This is true, Mother, we know it is! A team of young people called Voice of Youth have true stories that prove this Creator God really loves people. He also plans to come from His faraway home to earth. When He gets here He will take all who follow Him here far away to His beautiful country and give each a beautiful, clean home."

"We must go to see for ourselves if this is true," the mother told her daughters. "The village of Vulelua is only four hours walk from here. Maybe we can get relief from this constant itching."

Filled with a strong desire, they gladly walked the jungle paths to attend these Frontier Evangelism meetings. Never before had they heard the stories of Jesus or sang the songs of hope. Even though all three of them looked ugly, covered with black ringworm, the youth treated them with courtesy and kindness. Joy, love, and hope drew them back night after night. Each night they felt comforted by the promises they heard from God's book that this Jesus walked with them on the long, dark walk home.

Before long the devil priest of Aola discovered what the mother and girls did each day. He threatened, "If you are baptized and join that church, we will kill you." They knew he meant just that, but the love of God drew the trio back anyway.

On one of the last nights a young man made a call for all who wanted to give their lives to Jesus and follow His way of living to stand. This mother and her two daughters stood. Then he added, "If you want to join God's church in baptism, please come forward."

They joined a large group who stepped to the front.

That night as they walked home, the family felt uneasy with a strange premonition that something must be wrong. As they neared their village, they heard a rustling in the bushes. Four warriors carrying bush knives rushed toward them. Immediately the mother and her daughters knelt down on the trail pleading aloud, "Jesus, please save us."

Suddenly a large flock of birds that usually do not fly at night descended on these men. The birds dove and swooped down, pecking the men continuously. Finally they could do nothing but flee back to the village. The mother and her daughters went on to their home where they went to bed and slept soundly. But early the next morning the village chief came to their house.

"Where are the warriors who guarded your house last night?" he demanded. "Who are they? Where did they get the bright lights that shone around your house?"

Gladly the mother shared their story. "This God named Jesus promised that He would never leave nor forsake His faithful children. When we prayed He sent His shining angels to guard us through the night. He also sent the birds to drive away the men who came to kill us. You see, we now belong to the God of heaven and He loves to hear our prayers. His power far exceeds that of the devil. He keeps us safe."

Soon the mother and her daughters accepted baptism. Because they followed God's laws of health and cleanliness their ringworm infestation healed. In their humble manner they shared with their village friends what God had done for them and their sincere witness drew many to Jesus. Now Aola has an Adventist church made of jungle material. Joyfully they wait for Jesus to welcome them to the place He prepared just for them. He will say, "Come, sit with Me on my throne. Continue to tell your story of how Jesus saved you. God's children from the unfallen worlds will rejoice with you throughout all eternity."

16

VICTORY ON SAVO ISLAND

A young man stepped up to Pastor Ervin Ferris. "Pastor, my name is John Sota. I'm from Savo Island north of Guadalcanal. Possibly you remember how the United States Navy suffered tragedy around the waters of Savo Island. In just an hour the Japanese inflicted on the allies one of the worst defeats in World War II. I too, have a battle to fight on Savo. Please let me tell you why I need your help."

Pastor Ervin beckoned, "Come, let's sit down and talk. What is your need?"

"I grew up in a Catholic village. Recently I became a Seventh-day Adventist. As you know, in the Solomon Islands if a person changes their beliefs, they must leave that village and move to a village of that faith. I have a deep burden for my dear family for I want them to know the great joy and peace I have. I long to tell the story of Jesus to my people. However I know that none of the village people will accept me because I changed my faith. That's why I am coming to you for help. Could you help me to be a missionary to my own people."

"God has providentially opened a way to meet your need," Pastor Ferris said with a smile. "This week I received a letter from a friend in Australia. He sent me a check for $500 to be used for a special project. I think God planned that the project will be saving your family. I will send you $50 a month to care for some of your expenses."

So John went back to his home village on Savo island. Immediately he began to be persecuted, often by his own family. Gradually they admitted they believed the gospel story, but because of the bigotry in the village, they refused to respond to the call of the gospel.

Then one day someone who hated John put poison in his food. His parents found him unconscious. For lack of a boat, they laid him in a canoe and paddled across the sea that covered the Ironbottom Sound filled with sunken ships. They took him to the Honiara hospital in Guadalcanal. For two weeks John lay at death's door. Then slowly he recovered enough to return to Savo though still very weak. His family pleaded with him to tell the authorities, but he replied, "If my Jesus could forgive those who killed Him, then I can forgive those who poisoned me." Though he never returned to full health, he kept on quietly witnessing for His Lord, winning one after another. But progress seemed slow and most difficult.

A year after his poisoning, the Catholic church in Honiara heard of John's dedication on Savo so they sent a priest with a team of young people from the parish in Honiara. Because they could find no accommodations in the village, John invited five of these Catholic boys to stay at his house. He treated them royally, but continued to carry on the evangelistic meetings he'd been conducting in his own house. Some of these Catholic boys sat down and listened.

As John preached one evening, his father rushed to the front door and yelled, "John! Spear!" John leaped to one side and the spear intended to kill him thudded into the wall behind him.

His father and these Catholic boys immediately gave chase to try to catch the assailant. You can imagine their surprise when they not only caught him plus three or four young men and the Catholic priest. All were their own friends from the Catholic church in Honiara. The five young boys who stayed with John vowed they'd never set foot in a Catholic church again.

Even though John's family pleaded with him to take the matter to the authorities he insisted, "If my God can forgive them, so I can too." This news spread around the Catholic village and made a tremendous impression on the people. However, 16 years passed with John worshiping, mingling, talking, and witnessing to the villagers but there were few results.

In October 2005 a businessman, Ivan Gehmu, from Honiara became friends with John. Seeing the dedication John had for his village, Ivan decided to use his own finances to obtain the services of the new mission boat to go to Savo Island. He took with him many bales of clothes, several women from the Dorcas society, and a Youth for Christ singing team. The ladies distributed the clothing from house to house and the youth began a 31-night series of meetings using a young man named Matthew to give the nightly talks.

Once again the Catholic church heard of these evangelistic meetings so they again sent a priest over to Savo. To be sure the meetings could not succeed, the priest hired a rascal who rallied other hoodlums to harass and disrupt the meetings and cut down the building. With the priest they planned different tactics of harassment for each of the 31 days.

But God used the singing group to touch the heart of the rascal leader. Never before had he heard such wonderful music. The priest sat outside in the shadows and listened, too. Every night when the rascal came home his wife would say, "You're paid to disturb the meetings. Why didn't you do it?"

Night after night he replied, "I'll do it tomorrow night."

On the last night Matthew made a call for those who wanted to give their lives to Jesus to stand. The rascal stood with the others. When he came home that night he said to his wife, "I have a confession to make to you. Tonight I stood for baptism. I gave my heart to Jesus. I want to join the Seventh-day Adventist church and learn how to live like Jesus."

"I have a confession to make too," his wife told him. "Without your knowing it, I went every night and stayed in the darkness and listened. I also stood and gave my heart to Jesus tonight."

Their 15-year-old daughter heard what they said and spoke up. "I don't want to be left alone," she said. "I want to join too." That night John saw the results of the power of God and greatly rejoiced when 27 people from that Catholic village stood for baptism.

A week later, Ivan Gehmu arrived again in the mission boat with five bales of clothes. He gathered all 27 people who had said they wanted baptism and said, "Will you please come aboard, so we can take you to a nearby island. You can't stay on Savo for the angry people of your village have confiscated and torn all of your clothes except what you're wearing. They will continue to find ways to persecute you. You need to come with me."

John explained, "I want to take you to a quiet place so that I can study the Bible with you. You see, before you are baptized you must understand God's will for your life. That's why we have baptismal classes."

When they arrived on the island John distributed all the clothes Ivan had brought plus new clothes Ivan purchased on his own. Ivan also provided food and shelter. For one week these new converts enjoyed peace and quiet as they learned how to become children of their heavenly Father.

John's heart nearly burst with joy as the rascal shared his thoughts. "This week I've had a taste of heaven," he said with a big smile. "The mission boat took us away from ugliness and strife, like Jesus will take us to heaven in a cloud. There we'll sit at Jesus' feet and feel closer to Him than even the angels, for we have our own salvation story to tell. Our old clothes, torn and worn by sin, have been replaced by the robe of Christ's righteousness. God will change hate to love, and persecution to peace and acceptance. We're no longer dead in sins but raised up by His love. We'll all sit together with Jesus."

After a week the new believers returned to Savo. The mission boat anchored just outside their village and they all stood on the deck and sang, "We have decided to follow Jesus . . . no turning back."

The next Sabbath all 27 received baptism in the ocean. Afterward John made a call. "Are there any others who would like to follow Jesus?" Another 15 villagers came forward. God's Holy Spirit continued to work through them. A month after the second baptism, 60 more persons requested to learn more about Jesus so they could also be baptized and join the Adventist church.

All this because 16 years before a young boy came to Pastor Ferris and requested help to take the gospel to his home village in Savo.

———

While the Holy Spirit poured out God's blessings on Savo Island, God's power continued to reach across the Ironbottom Sound to the large island of Guadalcanal. Sometimes God can find no one like John to take the risk of persecution in order to tell the gospel story. This time He used the drawing power of the Holy Spirit to reach up to the high mountains in the center of the island to a heathen village.

God put a desire into the mind of a naked little boy who had never worn clothes because no one else in the village wore clothes. Living high above civilization, this young adventurous lad decided he wanted to go down to the valleys and experience the huge ocean he could see from afar. So he wandered away, farther than he'd ever gone down the mountains.

Nearing a village he heard sounds he had never heard before. Shyly he sneaked from tree to tree until he could see a large building through the bushes. Beneath its floor he saw an open area with many children sitting on board seats. Their singing sounded beautiful. Fascinated, he listened, wishing he could understand the words but he spoke a different dialect.

He hid there for three days, not knowing he had found a school, for none existed in his remote village. Then someone discovered him, treated him kindly, and cleaned him up. They gave him food for his hungry stomach and clothes to cover his nakedness, and allowed him to sleep in the classroom at night. Most of all the boy listened and loved the songs. Again and again his ears caught one word—"Jesus."

This name fascinated him. He finally understood that Jesus did not live in this village now but the people expected Him to come back soon.

Solomon Islanders seem to be born with the talent to sing, and the boy soon learned the tunes even though he could not understand the words. He stayed at the school for a week, listening and learning to sing with the children. Then he decided to return to his mountain village. When he arrived home he kept singing these songs. He knew the tunes but only remembered the word "Jesus." So he repeated that powerful name over and over in each song.

His grandfather, the village chief in that mountain region, demanded, "What are you singing and what is this Jesus?"

"He is a loving God, not like the devil. He is not at the village, but they expect Him to come back soon!"

"Well then, I'm going to go down and wait until He comes."

Grandfather found the Solo Saia School. He found someone who could understand his language. He stayed and waited there until he heard the story of Jesus. Thrilled he asked, "Will He take me home with Him when He comes, even if I'm living in my mountain village?"

"Yes, He will take you home with Him if you give your heart to Him. He loves you and wants you to tell the people living in the mountains of the true God and His love. But you can no longer worship heathen gods. You can't serve God and His enemy at the same time."

Grandfather smiled. "I will gladly change, for I have never been so happy. Will you come and teach our villagers, so we can learn to love this Jesus?"

Gladly the students at the school climbed up the mountain each week. They shared their faith and love for Jesus. The students taught the eager listeners the words to the tunes that they'd heard the little boy constantly singing. Quickly the heathen learned these songs of Jesus' love. They understood that they could go home with Him, too.

This happened in 2005. In July 2006 the village chief, his wife, the devil priest, and eight others were baptized. Now the villagers have joined together to build a jungle chapel to worship the God they now love.

All this because a naked little boy heard the name of Jesus in song. He shared that precious name continually until his grandfather longed to receive the power of His divine love. Think of the joy of the Father, Jesus, the Holy Spirit, and the angels as they plan for those dear people who never would have known the joys of salvation were it not for a little boy who sang, "Jesus, Jesus, Jesus," all day long.

17

THE RAY BOAT MIRACLE

From June to August the southeast trade winds blow hard in the Solomon Islands, making the seas very rough. Having just completed the final project of 2005, the Fly and Build team headed for Honiara. The capable skipper on the mission ship fought heavy seas trying to get into the calmer water of the Ironbottom Sound off Guadalcanal. Above the pounding of the sea as the ship hit wave after wave, the team heard assurance from the skipper's voice as he sang his favorite song, "Praise Him in the morning, praise Him in the noonday, praise Him when the sun goes down."

Behind their 53-foot mission ship they towed a 22-foot Sea Ray boat tied with three ropes. It was a beautiful craft, made of fiberglass and had a new 40-horsepower motor. The Sea Ray boat belonged to the Eastern Solomon Mission. Traveling in the wake of the ship with strong winds blowing from behind, the crew felt concern every time the it partially lifted out of the water.

About 9:00 p.m., the boat crew heard a loud *craaack*. The rope towing the Ray boat had snapped and the boat was floating free somewhere on the dark waters. With a quick prayer the skilled, experienced skipper, Lowell Lukizi, immediately turned the ship in a circle. Doing so, he placed the ship sideways to the waves. When the first wave hit, all 23 people on the Fly and Build team, trying to rest in the wheel house, were pitched from one side of the boat to the other. That hurt!

This happened again and again as the skipper did his best to get around to find the Ray boat. After much effort the spotlight helped them see it. As a crew member kept the spotlight on it, the ship circled again. All hands tried to catch hold of the ropes used to tow it, but in vain.

The spotlight also showed the huge crashing waves breaking on the coral reefs between the ship and the shore. Since human lives on the ship were in jeopardy, and are far more valuable than even a Sea Ray boat, they had to get away from the reefs as soon as possible.

Immediately five people gathered on the deck to pray that God would watch over this boat that belonged to the mission. The mission had limited funds and could not afford to replace it. But given the force of the wind and waves, without God's guidance it would be smashed to smithereens on the coral reef. Then the ship continued on, traveling at least half an hour before reaching a point of land that sheltered them from the wind.

The spotlight revealed they had anchored about 40 feet from shore. Two men from a nearby village rowed their canoes out to the ship. The skipper explained that they'd just lost the Ray boat they'd been hauling and asked anyone who saw it to let them know.

Eventually, two men returned. "We found your boat between the crashing waves and the beach floating in calm water," they said. "It's strange that it hadn't been overturned. The motor is in its place too. We can't understand why the winds and waves didn't drive it either to the sand or on the reef."

Everyone was thrilled. "If we give you a reward of A$200," the skipper called to the men, "could you start the motor and bring it to us in the morning?"

They agreed. Early the next morning people on the ship heard the welcome sound of the motor. The Ray boat arrived—the boat, the motor, and all the contents completely preserved.

"May we tell you how this boat was preserved?" the skipper asked the men who brought it. "Long ago, in 1920, a Christian missionary named Jugha, Kata Rangoso's brother, came to Choisuel. He told my grandfather about a God who is stronger than the devil. When I was born in 1957, my grandfather taught me to pray to this God who loves to help His children. So last night we all prayed to our God. Instantly God used His mighty hand of power to keep that boat safe. More than that, He guided the boat so that it seemed to follow us to the point behind which we sought shelter for the night. Then you came to us and He guided you to find it in the dark just three or four minutes travel from where we anchored. Would you like to know and serve a God that loves to do the impossible for His children?"

And the men answered, "Yes, please tell us more!"

Kopiu,
Devastated and Restored

Before World War II began Kopiu operated as a thriving mission station with clinic facilities, a productive farm and garden, a church, and a growing school. The European-style house remained on the hill. Then came the orders, "All White missionaries must evacuate immediately."

National leaders continued as best they could. Kata Rangoso with many capable helpers supervised the area around the New Georgia group near Batuna and the Marovo Lagoon. Sasa Rore took charge of the Kopiu school and Guadalcanal area. Progress on the mission station continued until the dreaded news came that the Japanese were advancing and would soon be there.

Students, teachers, workers, and people from the surrounding villages all fled in fear to the jungle and mountains. But before they left, the nationals removed or hid much of the equipment and valuables they felt would be of any benefit to the Japanese.

Just before the Japanese reached the Kopiu area, on that very day, a terrific storm swept through the mountains. The river through which the Japanese must cross flooded. Their armed forces got bogged down in the mud and could not proceed. Forced to return to their base, the Japanese never arrived at Kopiu. Previously the Allies left with the mission boats, except the *Portal* which the nationals hid in a jungle stream.

Because of the steep mountains in the center of Guadalcanal and the lack of roads, Kopiu needed a mission boat, for it was their only means of contact for supplies and mail with Honiara and Tulagi. After the war, for some reason the entire mission fleet, purchased with mission offerings, was sold. Without contact to the outside for news and supplies, the missionaries could not exist and soon moved away. The local people followed. Gradually the lovely lawn and flowers of Kopiu reverted again to forest. Soon one could not tell that a thriving mission station had ever been there. Only the large mango trees planted by the Ferrises hinted of the lovely home and grounds that once existed.

However, a small Adventist village remained on the flat area near the seashore. A primary school continued in a grass hut. The faithful members like Grandfather Solomon and Grandmother June George, who lived in their simple houses and worshiped in a native-built church, kept watch and guarded the unoccupied property. They believed that God still had a purpose for Kopiu in His grand future plans.

What happened to the European house, the home of Norman and Ruby Ferris and their four children, over the period of 10 years? Local people used the timbers to build a church at the bottom of the hill. They left only the cement foundations.

Some time after the war another church organization tried, through the government, to make claim to the property. Since the flat area was very fertile garden land and much had reverted to jungle, they stated that the SDA Church had no more interest in using the land for a mission. Because the mission had not kept records, it seemed they might lose these special 364 acres.

Again God took control. The original chief who had transacted the sale with Norman Ferris came forward with the original bill of sale document that contained both Norman's signature and the chief's thumbprint. He told the government that the land had been his. He firmly stated, "I gave this property to the Adventist Church. It will always belong to the Adventist Church."

In 1990 the government replaced the primary school with a brick building. All those years primary education had continued in a grass hut on the flats at the base of the old mission station. About that time a group of local community leaders approached the mission regarding the possibility of expanding the primary school to include a high school. They formed what they called the Kopiu Committee. Included were village representatives from Catholic, Anglican, South Sea Island Evangelicals, London Missionary Society, and the Uniting Church, which included Methodists, Presbyterians, and Congregationalists. All agreed that Kopiu would be an ideal spot for the high school. So they asked the mission leaders in Honiara for permission to build on the Kopiu property. They stated that all agreed that the school principal and teachers must be Seventh-day Adventists and the high school would be operated by the standards of that church. However, the original plans to build proved too broad and costly. For a time all plans were shelved.

Not until 2003 did Ervin Ferris hear of the committee's desire to build a high school at Kopiu. With the Fly and Build team he stopped at the mission office in Honiara. The builders had just completed a project, and while waiting for their flight home to Australia they heard a conversation concerning the desire to build a high school at Kopiu.

Instantly God put the thought in Ervin's mind, *I want your team to become involved.*

Ervin sent a silent prayer to God. *You know I have no funds, no money, and there is only a little in the fund-raising account.*

But God answered back in his mind, *You know that money is no problem to Me. I love to do the impossible. I will give you ideas and faith to go ahead. It's no problem for Me to supply all the materials for this building.*

As soon as possible, Ervin applied to the Canadian government for a grant from their aid program. He received a reply that they would supply funds to build a two-story building with four classrooms, a library, two computer rooms, and two storerooms. The space below could later be used for teaching manual arts. With great joy that God could use him to restore the school his father had started, Ervin and his wife, Val, went ahead in faith and purchased all the supplies for this building

In December they received word from the Canadian government that there had been an upheaval in their aid program. All projects had been put on hold. This left them in a tough financial spot. On their knees Val and Ervin decided to fund this project from their retirement nest egg. That year God blessed their Fly and Build mango picking project and gave them the best season ever for high quality, quantity, and sales. Much hard work resulted in more supplies for the Solomon Island projects.

The local people living around Kopiu, from the various Protestant and Catholic churches, cleared the land at the bottom of the hill. They also cut and prepared some of the needed lumber. The government agreed to pay the teachers' salaries and expenses.

But Satan spread a false rumor that devils occupied the hill. Because of the prevalence of devil worship in the Solomon Islands, many of the SDA church members refused to even walk on the hill, for they felt that the land had become devil-possessed. So in 2005, before the building began, church leaders and Fly and Build volunteers climbed the hill to rededicate the property back to the Lord again. Standing in the presence of God, they invited the Holy Spirit to take full control. They left that hillside knowing that God's power will fill the hearts and minds of each person connected with the school who submits to God. What a promise! "Resist the devil and he will flee from you" (James 4:7).

Now the time had come. People from surrounding villages helped cut down and prepare the timber that grew on the 364-acre property. The Fly and Build team worked hard and erected the two-story building named Kopiu Adventist Secondary School.

Norman Ferris's youngest daughter, Marilyn Peaty, and his oldest daughter, Norma Crabtree, volunteered to be in charge of the cookhouse, preparing the meals for the team of builders. Food supplies ran low as they neared the end of the project. Thirty workers had just finished the midday meal, and as the sisters began cleaning up, they saw a boat dock and people getting in the dinghy to come ashore. (Interested villagers and their religious leaders came from near and far to watch a school of that standard being built in 11 days. Hearing of the rapid progress, they came to see for themselves.)

At the same time that the tourist group was docking, a group of men who'd been milling timber all night and till noon arrived. "We're hungry!" the said. "Haven't had any food."

Someone sent the sisters this message: "Get ready to feed them all."

Marilyn and Norma knew their food supply was almost gone. The pots were nearly empty. How could they be hospitable and invite 15 more people to eat from the meager leftovers. Knowing they had very little available food, they bowed their heads and prayed together. "Dear God, these people will soon be coming up the hill. The rice is almost gone, and there's only a small amount of vegetable stew left. What shall we do?"

At that moment God gave them the thought, *Remember how the widow always had meal and oil to feed Elijah, herself, and her son? Jesus had no trouble feeding more than 5,000 people with five loaves and two fishes. Aren't you serving the same God? What He did long ago, He will do for you now if you trust Him. Go forward in faith!*

Marilyn and Norma thanked God and began to warm the leftovers. As they saw the people coming up the hill, they set out the plates and in perfect trust knew God would supply enough food.

As they met their guests with sweet smiles, they invited, "Please, come and enjoy what God has given us to eat." All gladly accepted the invitation.

They began dishing out the food. As the sisters filled plate after plate, the supply did not stop. Everyone had plenty. Best of all, the people from the combined Presbyterian, Methodist, and Congregational church experienced the love and hospitality of Christ because the daughters of Norman Ferris trusted God.

As Marilyn and Norma scraped the pots and pans to save the generous amount of leftovers, Norma exclaimed, "Wouldn't Dad be happy if he knew what just happened! We're standing near the place where he prayed for each sick person he treated."

"Yes. He lived expecting God to do the impossible," Marilyn said as tears of joy trickled down her cheeks. "By his example Dad taught us kids to expect miracles."

With arms around each other, the sisters bowed their heads,

"We praise You for a dad who always depended on You. Thank you for giving us this miracle! We also praise You for beginning to restore Kopiu."

In early 2006, almost before the paint was dry in the classrooms, 41 secondary students enrolled. Over half came from faiths other than Seventh-day Adventist. All joined together to study the Bible. When school closed that year five students asked to be baptized.

Plans stated that each year the next level of high school be added. In 2007 the principal estimated an enrollment of 120 students. More important, the original purpose of Kopiu, when it began in the 1930s, was to lead the youth in this part of Guadalcanal to know and love Christ.

Because many students come from a considerable distance, the need for dormitories to house them became essential. An interested donor from the United States provided the money for a girls' dormitory. In June 2006 Fly and Build completed the girls' dormitory with nine rooms that care for 72 girls.

The same donors provided for a boys' dormitory which was built during the interim of February 5-27, 2007, by Maranatha Volunteers International, located in Sacramento, California. The Fly and Build team joined them. Fifteen rooms house 120 young men. God has provided the only high school on the entire "weather coast" of Guadalcanal.

In 2008 the Fly and Build team erected a beautiful little church at the top of the path. It was constructed of native timber cut and sawed from the school land. To finance this, three island men joined with Val and Ervin Ferris in a mango picking project in North Queensland, Australia. Their willing hands picked 6,500 boxes of mangoes. The money they earned, plus US$5,000 from two people who love this school, covered the expenses of building a beautiful chapel. Here God's faithful children on the "weather side" of Guadalcanal are worshipping from Sabbath to Sabbath till Jesus comes to take them home.

Only the angels have kept a record of God's faithful workers who have been used by Him to bless others at Kopiu. He knows each one who planted the 20,000 coconut trees currently bearing prolifically. He can name each child and adult that weeded the gardens that fed the students and teachers. He sent angels to protect the villagers from accidents when they cut down the huge trees and sawed them into lumber for each building. He heard the first prayers of students from devil-worshiping homes asking for courage to step out and belong to God. He saw the villagers who kept watch when greedy people tried to steal the land. He listened as teachers pleaded with God to give them wisdom to reach the hearts of their students. He healed the many sick who climbed the hill and waited patiently on the grass for Norman Ferris to bring help and healing as he sat under his house perched on a box. He stayed by Ruby as she grabbed her medical kit and hurried to a home where a mother needed her help to give birth.

Yes, God's presence and the power of the Holy Spirit kept watch over this precious property from the moment Norman and Ruby Ferris landed on the beach, and erected a native type home in 1931. Someday soon this little world, so troubled with evil and tormented with suffering, will be governed by King Jesus and His faithful earth children. Meeting around God's throne Jesus Christ will say, "Come My children, and take your places near Me around My throne."

Then Jesus will step down and take Norman's and Ruby's hands, one on each side, and lead them to their thrones. He will beckon the thousands who learned of the love of God throughout the Solomon Islands, to come sit with them. What a glorious family reunion! All God's children are finally home!